Great Folk Tales & Fairy Tales of Ireland

Compiled and Introduced by
Mary McGarry
Illustrations by
Richard Hook

LEOPARD

This omnibus edition published in 1996 by Leopard Books,
a division of Random House (UK) Limited,
20 Vauxhall Bridge Road, London SW1V 2SA

Copyright © Mary McGarry 1996

Great Folk Tales of Ireland published by Muller in 1979
Great Fairy Tales of Ireland published by Muller in 1979

The right of Mary McGarry to be identified as author of
this work has been asserted by her in accordance with the
Copyright, Designs and Patents Act, 1988.

ISBN 0 7529 0208 3

Great Folk Tales
of Ireland

Contents

	PAGE
INTRODUCTION	7
THE FATE OF THE CHILDREN OF LIR *Joseph Jacobs*	11
FIOR USGA *T. Crofton Croker*	17
THE WHITE TROUT: A LEGEND OF CONG *Samuel Lover*	21
THE BOYHOOD OF CUCHULAINN (9th century) *Translated by Standish Hayes O'Grady*	25
THE KILDARE POOKA *Patrick Kennedy*	29
HOW CORMAC MacART WENT TO FAERY *Joseph Jacobs*	33
THE BREWERY OF EGG-SHELLS *T. Crofton Croker*	39
THE STORY OF DEIRDRE *Joseph Jacobs*	43
HOW THE SHANNON ACQUIRED ITS NAME *Patrick Kennedy*	57
THE KING AND THE BISHOP *Samuel Lover*	59
FIN MacCUMHAIL AND THE SON OF THE KING OF ALBA *Jeremiah Curtin*	69
THE FIANNA (15th or 16th Century) *Translated by Standish Hayes O'Grady*	77

DIARMUID AND GRAINNE
Adapted by Mary McGarry   *81*

OISIN IN TIR NA NOG
P. W. Joyce   *87*

ST. BRIGID'S CLOAK
Patrick Kennedy   *97*

THE GIANT'S STAIRS
T. Crofton Croker   *99*

THE CROOKENED BACK
T. Crofton Croker   *107*

Note: For the names of the characters, the spelling used is that of the original story. The spelling therefore sometimes varies from story to story.

Introduction

Story-telling has always been an intrinsic part of the Celtic way of life, an amusement as old as the race itself. The narratives, peopled with both deities and mortals who dwell in a land of adventure, warfare and romance, form perhaps one of the oldest vernacular literatures of any European nation. The Celtic realm is a veritable treasure trove for the keen folklorist, and indeed for all who enjoy an exciting fireside tale.

The monastic scribe of the late Middle Ages preserved much of this heritage of lore in the ornate, vellum manuscripts of "The Book of Leinster" or "The Book of the Dun Cow". But it is the strong oral tradition of the Irish people which has enabled a living folklore to survive. Over the centuries story-telling was an esteemed profession. Poets, bards and "seanachai" (Gaelic story-tellers) who enjoyed the privileged patronage of the Irish chiefs, were an essential part of any festive gathering, where they recited poems and tales for the entertainment of the guests. The influence of alien cultures and the expansion of modern life has unfortunately led to the decline of this class, and the number of "seanachai" today is rapidly dwindling. Luckily the wealth of their memories will be saved for future generations in the archives of the Irish Folklore Commission, which since 1935 has systematically collected and annotated these native sources.

Peig Sayers (1873–1958) is perhaps the best known of this "dying race"; a native of the Blasket Islands off the Dingle peninsula, she could in her time recount no fewer than three hundred and seventy-five narratives. To find the real culture of modern Ireland one must look to her folklore, for here in stories handed down from age to age are endless clues to the great mythological epics of the past.

The shades of prehistory can be lifted by a study of some of the folk tradition, because scholarship has established a reasonable historical basis for several well-known tales. But whether factual or fictitious, the accounts give free rein to the fertile Celtic imagination. The Ulster and Fenian cycles are possibly in character the most spectacular section of Irish legends and are certainly the most popular. The events of the Ulster cycle revolve around the ancient kingdom of the same name and are approximately dated to the first century before Christ. Cuchulainn, the central hero, plays an important role in the victory of the North over Maeve, Queen of Connaught. The inclusion of an excerpt from the boyhood deeds of this warrior gives an idea of his stature in Irish folklore.

In "The Book of Leinster" lies the most famous single story of the Ulster cycle, "The story of Deirdre", a source of inspiration for Yeats, Synge and others. The narrative, which relates the tragic fate of Deirdre and her lover Naois at the hands of Deirdre's betrothed, Connachar, King of Ulster, shows many similarities to the story of Tristan and Iseult, and the other great romance of the Fenian cycle, that of Diarmuid and Grainne. It is also known as one of "The Three Sorrowful Tales of Erin", along with "The Fate of the Children of Lir". The legend of the transformation by magic of Lir's family into wild swans has its counterparts in other popular European mythologies.

The Fenian cycle, traditionally assigned to the third century A.D., depicts the adventures of the band of warriors known as the "Fianna". Their leader, Finn MacCumhail, is just one of a host of heroic figures portrayed for Irish children. Oisin, Finn's son, is the subject of both prose and poetry, which describe his journey to the land of eternal youth, "Tir na nOg". The rigorous requirements for entry into the "Fianna" illustrate the fact that it was no mean feat to be included in its membership, and might make it comparable to the legendary Arthur and his "Knights of the Round Table".

Irish folklore is not restricted to the heroic but covers a wide range of traditions. The hauntings of the "Pooka" mingle with tales of fairy changelings, or the imaginative origin of the Lough of Cork, as told in Crofton Croker's "Fior Usga". Samuel Lover relates anecdotes collected on a visit to Clonmacnoise in "The King and the Bishop" which, if slightly stage-Irish in character, nevertheless shows the vitality of Irish local tradition and humour.

In any collection such as this one feels that merely the tip of the iceberg is being touched; only a taste provided to arouse one's interest. However, I hope that this introduction to what Yeats aptly termed "The Celtic Twilight" may encourage the reader to delve more deeply into a world, the limits of which still lie in the hazy Irish mist.

Mary McGarry
Dublin, May 1972

The Fate of the Children of Lir

BY JOSEPH JACOBS

I t happened that a long time ago in the age of gods and heroes, the Sea God, Lir, married a foster-daughter of Bodb the Red, King of the gods. She bore him four children; a daughter called Fionula, then a son called Aed and two others, twin boys, called Fiachra and Conn. But at the birth of the twins she died and Lir was left sorrowing.

After some time Lir visited the court of his father-in-law and married the sister of his dead wife, whom he thought would be a good mother to his children. For a time all went well. The princess, called Aeife, treated her stepchildren kindly. But then Aeife began to be jealous of the tenderness and attention shown by Lir to Fionula and her brothers, and to fear he loved them better than he did her. At last the wish for their death came into her heart and she began to plot to destroy them.

First she tried to bribe the servants to murder them, but this failed. Fearing to kill them herself, she led them away to a lonely lake, where she sent them into the water to bathe. Then from under her cloak she drew out a wand, such as the Druids used, and making an incantation over the children she turned them all into swans.

But although she had enough magical power to change their shapes, she could not take from them their speech or human hearts.

Fionula, the lovely girl who was now a swan, swam into the reeds just below the bank where Aeife was standing, and rearing her proud head she said: "Wicked and treacherous woman, give us back our human shapes, or Lir our father will punish you."

But Aeife smiled scornfully. "The lake is deep, and the children

11

of Lir were drowned," she said. "That is the story I shall tell their father."

No words of beseeching would change the wicked Aeife's heart, or make her withdraw the spell.

Fionula spoke once more. "How long must we remain swans?" she asked bravely.

"Better if you had not asked me," replied Aeife. "But I will tell you. Three hundred years shall you remain upon this lake; and three hundred years upon the Sea of Moyle, the sea which lies between Erin and Alba; and three hundred years more beside the Isle of Glora in Erris."

"If you had killed us," cried Aed, "it had been kinder!"

"Nay," replied Aeife, "for after this moment you shall not remember your grief at being swans. But your human speech and human hearts, these shall you keep and you shall be able to sing more sweetly and more softly than swans have ever yet sung. Fare you well. I could have loved you had not your father loved you too dearly."

And with one wild gesture, half triumphant, half tragic, Aeife turned her back upon the lake and upon the four swans. But as she mounted the hill that lay between the lake and her palace she heard the swans singing, singing so sweetly and so softly that for a moment she paused to listen and then, plunging her fingers into her ears, she hurried on.

When Aeife got home she found Lir waiting for her. "You have been gone long," he said, "you and the children."

Aeife began to weep and wail of how the children had been disobedient and how they had drowned in the strong current and reeds in the lake.

But Lir in great grief cried out: "This is not true! You who pretended to love my children with a mother's love, you have led them away, you have led them away!" Here he was able to say no more, but rushed away from Aeife and ran towards the lake.

The lake lay shimmering like silver under the beams of the summer moon. And as he stood there, four swans came sailing towards him, their wings widened as if to enfold him. And one, the one who had been his daughter, began to speak in the tones he loved so well. She told him all the tragic story, and Conn, the youngest of the twins, broke in, begging his father to restore their human shape.

"I want to run and play with my brother," he said. "Just as we used to run and play before magic touched us."

Then Lir wrung his hands in agony. "Would that I had power enough," he said sorrowfully. "But I am, after all, such a puny god, I who had thought I ruled the sea."

"Do not grieve, my lord," said Fionula very gently. "We are not so unhappy. We love you and remember you are our father. If you will come down every night at sunset, then we will talk to you; then we will sing to you, and you will forget."

But anger against the false woman Aeife arose again in the heart of the Sea God. He caressed the heads of the swans, and his tears fell fast as he turned to leave them, and even their song which followed him up the hillside could not soothe his rage.

He went to Bodb the Red, who asked for proof of the evil deed. Lir led him to the lake, where the swans floated in the red light of the dawn. And they told their own tale, without passion or anger, until the end came and the toll of their sentence—three hundred years upon the Lake of Darvra, three hundred years upon the Sea of Moyle, three hundred years beside the Isle of Glora.

Lir asked Bodb to use his magic to bring back his children. But Bodb the Red turned to him a face of pain and pity and said sadly that his magic too was not enough to restore them to their father.

Yet Bodb the Red could punish Aeife. She came before the King quietly, as one in deep sorrow. She had put away her jewels, and over her golden hair she wore the veil of mourning.

The King began to tell her the story of the swans, while Aeife boldly pretended that the children had been claimed by the waters of the lake.

The King twirled his Druid's wand and said: "I shall not ask you, Aeife, what has become of the children of Lir. I shall not ask you what you can do to restore them to their sorrowing father. He stands there, you can look at him and see how stricken he is. You can listen, Aeife, for the soft voice of Fionula, and look long for the lithe form of young Aed to stride over the fairy hills. You can run fleet of foot across the green grass, but never again will Conn or Fiachra overtake you, or their gay young laughter gladden your heart. But my question is far away from talk of the lost children of Lir. Answer me truly, Aeife, what do you fear more than my wand?"

Aeife, in great terror at the wand waving above her head, was compelled to answer: "To be a demon, a demon of the air, with no rest for body or soul."

She shrieked wildly, and she tried to clutch the wand, but it swept over her like the sword of an avenger, and her human shape fell from her like a beautiful dress. Then she rose as if she had wings, the wings of a vampire or a great bat, and again she shrieked, like a shrill wind before a storm, and flew far away. Over the hills she went, and over the Lake of Darvra. The sky was black with clouds, and from the distant mountains came the heavy roll of thunder. No heart, no speech, no song had the King of the gods left her—only her wickedness, and a demon's shape to carry her about for ever like a bird of ill omen.

All the gods of the Gaels came to hear of the sweet singing of the swans and went down to the Lake of Darvra to listen to it. It became a custom amongst gods and mortals to hold a yearly feast in honour of the swans.

But at the end of three hundred years the second part of the spell began. The swans had to leave the beautiful lake they knew so well, and fly away to the cold north to make their home upon the bleak and stormy Sea of Moyle.

Upon the Sea of Moyle, far away from gods and men, the four swans suffered the worst of weather. In lonely exile they spent day and night buffeted by wind and storm, haunted by the cries of ship-wrecked mariners and terrified by the monsters of the deep. Forbidden to land, their feathers in the bitter winters froze against the sharp rocks, and only their love for each other remained of the happy past.

During this sad time Fionula, the eldest of the four, became as a mother to the rest, wrapping her plumage round the youngest ones when the frost left a white rime on the rocks. With Conn on her right hand always, and Fiachra on her left, she kept Aed in front of her. "For," she said, "so I can shelter you all with my wings."

At last they entered on the third stage of their ordeal and went to the wild Isle of Glora; and there, too, they suffered loneliness and fear. The years rolled by. On the shores of Erris they first heard the sound of a church bell, which filled them with wonder.

As the time of their sentence drew to an end, they wished to return to the palace of their father Lir. Soon the air was filled with the sound of wings in strong flight, as the four swans winged their way towards Ireland. But when they came to look for their old home, all they could see was a few great mounds, clumps of nettles and windswept bushes. The palace was there, but from their eyes it was hidden, because they were destined for higher things than a return to the land of their youth.

With great sadness they flew slowly back to Erris, and then again they heard the thin sound of a bell. Terrified, the swans listened. The bell stopped and from a tiny chapel a man dressed in the robe of a hermit came out and made his way down towards them on the shore. The old hermit heard their story and the four swans made their home beside the little chapel and every day said over the simple prayers that he taught them. Their sorrow lightened; their beautiful song was heard again.

Now it happened that a Princess of Munster was to wed a powerful chief, and begged from him as a bridal token the four wonderful swans that sung so well. The chief tried to bribe the hermit to part with the swans with gifts of bronze and silver for the chapel.

But the old man waved him away saying: "There is no price for a human soul. Under their plumage beat human hearts. Enchantment is still heavy upon them, but God is merciful, and their penance draws nigh to its end."

However, the chief seized hold of the silver chains which coupled the swans and dragged them away. But when the swans were ordered to sing before the bride, not a note could they utter. Then the face of the princess froze stiff in horror, for from the four swans fell away their snowy plumage and before her cowered an aged woman and three withered old men. Nine hundred years had passed over their heads and the days of gods and heroes had gone for ever. The bride ran shrieking from the palace.

But the hermit, seeing that the Angel of Death would soon claim them, sprinkled each meek white head with the water of holiness, and to each gave promise of life everlasting.

Fionula stretched out her arms towards the other three, and asked that they be laid in one grave, with Conn placed on her right hand and Fiachra on her left, and Aed before her face where she could see him. So that with her wings she could shelter them, as she had done upon the stormy Sea of Moyle.

Thus did the hermit lay the four children of Lir to rest at last.

Fior Usga

BY T. CROFTON CROKER

a little way beyond the Gallows Green of Cork, and just outside the town, there is a great lough of water, where people in the winter go and skate for the sake of diversion. But the sport above the water is nothing to what is under it, because at the very bottom of this lough there are buildings and gardens far more beautiful than any now to be seen. And how they came there was in this manner.

Long before Saxon foot pressed Irish ground there was a great King, called Corc, whose palace stood where the lough is now, in a round green valley that was just a mile about. In the middle of the courtyard was a spring of fair water, so pure and so clear that it was the wonder of all the world. Much did the King rejoice at having so great a curiosity within his palace, but as people came in crowds from far and near to draw the precious water of this spring, he was sorely afraid that in time it might become dry.

So he caused a high wall to be built up around it, and would allow nobody to have the water, which was a very great loss to the poor people living about the palace. Whenever he wanted any for himself he would send his daughter to get it, not liking to trust his servants with the key of the well-door, fearing they might give some of the water away.

One night the King gave a grand entertainment, and there were many great princes present, and lords and nobles without end. There were wonderful doings throughout the palace: there were bonfires, whose blaze reached up to the very sky; and dancing was there, to such sweet music that it ought to have waked up the dead out of their graves; and feasting was there in the greatest of plenty for all who came; nor was anyone turned away from the palace gates, but "you're welcome—you're welcome heartily," was the porter's salute for all.

Now it happened at this grand entertainment there was one young prince above all the rest mighty comely to behold, and as tall and as straight as ever eye would wish to look on. Right merrily did he dance that night with the old King's daughter, wheeling there, as light as a feather, and footing it away to the admiration of everyone. The musicians played the better for seeing their dancing; and they danced as if their lives depended upon it.

After all this dancing came the supper, and the young prince was seated at table by the side of his beautiful partner, who smiled upon him as often as he wished, for he had constantly to turn to the company and thank them for the many compliments passed upon his fair partner and himself.

In the midst of this banquet one of the great lords said to King Corc, "May it please your majesty, here is everything in abundance that heart can wish for, both to eat and drink, except water."

"Water!" said the King, mightily pleased at someone calling for that of which purposely there was a want. "Water shall you have, my lord, speedily, and that of such a delicious kind that I challenge all the world to equal it. Daughter," said he, "go and fetch some in the golden vessel which I caused to be made for the purpose."

The King's daughter, who was called Fior Usga (which signifies "Spring Water" in English), did not much like to be told to perform so menial a service before so many people; and though she did not venture to refuse the commands of her father, yet she hesitated to obey him, and looked down upon the ground.

The King, who loved his daughter very much, seeing this was sorry for what he had desired her to do, but having said the word he was never known to recall it. He therefore thought of a way to make his daughter go speedily to fetch the water, and this was by proposing that the young prince, her partner, should go along with her.

Accordingly, in a loud voice, he said, "Daughter, I wonder not at your fearing to go alone so late at night; but I doubt not the young prince at your side will go with you."

The prince was not displeased at hearing this and, taking the golden vessel in one hand, with the other he led the King's daughter out of the hall so gracefully that all present gazed after them with delight.

When they came to the spring of water, in the courtyard of the palace, the fair Usga unlocked the door with the greatest care. But

18

stooping down with the golden vessel to take some of the water out of the well, she found the vessel so heavy that she lost her balance and fell in. The young prince tried to save her, but in vain, because the water rose and rose so fast that the entire courtyard was speedily covered with it, and he hastened back almost in a state of distraction to the King.

The door of the well being left open the water, so long confined, rejoiced at obtaining its liberty and rushed forth incessantly, every moment rising higher; it reached the hall of the entertainment sooner than the young prince himself, so that when he attempted to speak to the King he was up to his neck in water. At length the water rose to such a height that it filled the entire green valley in which the King's palace stood, and so the present Lough of Cork was formed.

Yet the King and his guests were not drowned, as would now happen if such an inundation were to take place. Neither was his daughter, the fair Usga, who returned to the banquet hall the very next night after this dreadful event. And every night since then the same entertainment and dancing goes on in the palace in the bottom of the lough, and it will last until someone has the luck to bring up out of it the golden vessel which was the cause of all the mischief.

Nobody can doubt that it was a judgment upon the King for his shutting up the well in the courtyard from the poor people. And if there are any who do not credit my story, they might go and see the Lough of Cork, for there it is to be seen to this day. The road to Kinsale passes at one side of it and when its waters are low and clear the tops of towers and stately buildings may be plainly viewed in the bottom by those who have good eyesight, without the help of spectacles.

The White Trout: A Legend of Cong

BY SAMUEL LOVER

*t*here was wanst upon a time, long ago, a beautiful lady who lived in a castle upon the lake beyant, and they say she was promised to a King's son, and they wor to be married, when all of a sudden he was murthered, the crathur (Lord help us), and threwn into the lake above, and so, of course, he couldn't keep his promise to the fair lady—and more's the pity.

Well, the story goes that she went out iv her mind, bekase av loosin' the King's son—for she was tendher-hearted, God help her, like the rest iv us!—and pined away after him, until at last, no one about seen her, good or bad; and the story wint that the fairies took her away.

Well, sir, in coorse o' time, the White Throut, God bless it, was seen in the sthrame beyant, and sure the people didn't know what to think av the crathur, seein' as how a white throut was never heard av afor, nor since. For years upon years the throut was there, just where you seen it this blessed minit, longer nor I can tell—aye throth, and beyant the memory o' th' ouldest in the village.

At last the people began to think it must be a fairy—for what else could it be? And no hurt nor harm was iver put an the white throut, until some wicked sinners of sojers kem to these parts, and laughed at all the people, and gibed and jeered them for thinkin' o' the likes. One o' them in partic'lar (bad luck to him; God forgi' me for saying it!) swore he'd catch the throut and ate it for his dinner—the blackguard.

Well, what would you think o' the villainy of the sojer? Sure enough he cotch the throut, and away wid him home, and puts an the fryin'-pan, and into it he pitches the purty little thing. The throut squeeled all as one as a christian crathur, and, my dear, you'd think the sojer id split his sides laughin'—for he was a harden'd villain. When he thought one side was done, he turns it over to fry the other, and, what would you think, but the devil a taste of a burn was an it at all. Sure the sojer thought it was a quare throut that could not be briled. "But," says he, "I'll give it another turn by-and-by," little thinkin' what was in store for him, the haythen.

Well, when he thought that side was done he turns it agin, and lo and behold you, the divil a taste more done that side was nor the other. "Bad luck to me," says the sojer, "but that bates the world," says he. "But I'll thry you agin, my darlint," says he, "as cunnin' as you think yourself."

And so with that he turns it over and over, but not a sign of the fire was on the purty throut. "Well," says he, "my jolly little throut, maybe you're fried enough, though you don't seem over-well dress'd; but you may be better than you look, like a singed cat, and a tit-bit afther all," says he.

With that he ups with his knife and fork to taste a piece o' the throut. But, my jew'l, the minit he puts his knife into the fish, there was a murtherin' screech, that you'd think the life id lave you if you hurd it. Away jumps the throut out av the fryin'-pan into the middle o' the flure and an the spot where it fell, up riz a lovely lady—the beautifullest crathur that eyes ever seen, dressed in white, and a band o' gold in her hair, and a sthrame o' blood runnin' down her arm.

"Look where you cut me, you villain," says she, and she held out her arm to him—and, my dear, he thought the sight id lave his eyes.

"Couldn't you lave me cool and comfortable in the river where you snared me, and not disturb me in my duty?" says she.

Well, he thrimbled like a dog in a wet sack, and at last he stammered out somethin', and begged for his life, and ax'd her lady-ship's pardon, and said he didn't know she was on duty, or he was too good a sojer not to know bether nor to meddle wid her.

"I was on duty, then," says she. "I was watchin' for my true love that is comin' by wather to me," says the lady, "an' if he comes while I'm away, an' that I miss iv him, I'll turn you into a pinkeen, and I'll hunt you up and down for ever more, while the grass grows or wather runs."

Well, the sojer thought the life id lave him, at the thoughts iv his bein' turned into a pinkeen, and begged for mercy.

And with that says the lady: "Renounce your evil coorses," says she, "you villain, or you'll repint it too late. Be a good man for the futher and go to your duty reg'lar. And now," says she, "take me back and put me into the river again, where you found me."

"Oh, my lady," says the sojer, "how could I have the heart to drownd a beautiful lady like you?"

But before he could say another word, the lady was vanished, and there he saw the little throut an the ground. Well, he put it in a clean plate, and away he runs for the bare life, for fear her lover would come while she was away. And he run, and he run, even till he came to the cave agin, and threw the throut into the river. The minit he did, the wather was as red as blood for a little while, by rayson av the cut, I suppose, until the sthrame washed the stain away; and to this day there's a little red mark an the throut's side, where it was cut.

Well, sir, from that day out the sojer was an altered man, and reformed his ways, and went to his duty reg'lar, and fasted three times a-week—though it was never fish he tuk an fastin' days, for afther the fright he got, fish id never rest an his stomach—savin' your presence.

But anyhow, he was an altered man, as I said before, and in coorse o' time he left the army, and turned hermit at last. They say he used to pray evermore for the soul of the White Throut.

The Boyhood of Cuchulainn

TRANSLATED BY
STANDISH HAYES O'GRADY

*t*his boy," said Fergus, "was reared in his father's and mother's house, by the seaside northwards in the plain of Muirthemne, where someone gave him an account of the macrad or 'boy-corps' of Emain Macha; how that Conchobar divides his day into three parts:

"the first being devoted to watching the boy-corps at their sport, especially that of hurling;

"the second to the playing of chess and draughts;

"the third to pleasurable consuming of meat and drink until drowsiness sets in, which then is promoted by the exertions of minstrels and musicians to induce favourable placidity of mind and disposition.

"And, for all that we are banished from him," continued Fergus, "by my word I swear that neither in Ireland nor in Scotland is there a warrior his (i.e., Conchobar's) counterpart.

"The little lad, then, as aforesaid, having heard of all this, one day told his mother that he was bent on a visit to Emain Macha to test the boy-corps at their own sports. She objected that he was immature, and ought to wait until some grown warrior or other, or some confidential of Conchobar's should, in order to insure his safety, bind over the boy-corps to keep the peace toward him. He told his mother that that was too long an outlook, that he could not wait, and that all she had to do was to set him a course for Emain Macha, since he did not know in which direction it lay.

" 'It is a weary way from here,' said the mother, 'for between thee and it lies Sliab Fuait.'

" 'Give me the bearings,' said he; and she did so.

"Away he went then, taking with him his hurly of brass, his ball of silver, his throwing javelin, and his toy spear, with which equipment he fell to shortening the way for himself. He did it thus: with his hurly he would strike the ball and drive it a great distance; then he pelted the hurly after it, and drove it just as far again; then he threw his javelin, lastly the spear. Which done, he would make a playful rush after them all, pick up the hurly, the ball and the javelin, while, before the spear's tip could touch the earth, he had caught the missile by the other end.

"In due course Cuchulainn reached Emain Macha, where he found the boy-corps, thrice fifty in number, hurling on the green and practising martial exercises with Conchobar's son, Fallomain, at their head. The lad dived right in among them and took a hand in the game. He got the ball between his legs and held it there, not suffering it to travel higher up than his knees or lower down than his ankle-joints, and so making it impossible for them to get in a stroke or in any other way to touch it.

"In utter amazement the whole corps looked on, but Follamain mac Conchobar cried: 'Good now, boys, all together meet this youngster as he deserves, and kill him; because it is taboo to have such a one join himself to you and interfere in your game, without first having had the civility to procure your guarantee that his life should be respected. Together then and at once attack him and avenge violation of your taboo; for we know that he is the son of some petty Ulster warrior, such as without safe-conduct is not accustomed to intrude into your play.'

"The whole of them assailed Cuchulainn, and simultaneously sent their hurlies at his head. He, however, parried all the hundred and fifty and was unharmed. The same with the balls, which he fended off with fists, fore-arms, and palms alone. Their thrice fifty toy spears he received in his little shield, and still was unhurt. In turn now, Cuchulainn went among them, and laid low fifty of the best. Five more of them," said Fergus, "came past the spot where myself and Conchobar sat at chess-play, with the young lad close in their wake.

" 'Hold, my little fellow,' said Conchobar, 'I see this is no gentle game thou playest with the boy-corps.'

" 'And good cause I have too,' cried Cuchulainn. 'After coming out of a far land to them, I have not had a guest's reception.'

" 'How now, little one,' said the King, 'knowest thou not the boy-corps conditions? That a newcomer must have them bounded by their honour to respect his life?'

" 'I knew it not,' said the boy, 'otherwise I had conformed, and taken measures beforehand.'

" ' 'Tis well,' said the king, 'take it now upon yourselves to let the boy go safe.'

" 'We do,' the boy-corps answered.

" 'They resumed play. Cuchulainn did as he would with them, and again laid out fifty of them on the ground. Their fathers deemed they could not but be dead. No such thing, however; it was merely that with his blows and pushes and repeated charges, he so terrified them that they took to the grass.

" 'What on earth is he at with them now?' asked Conchobar.

" 'I swear by my gods,' said Cuchulainn, 'that until they in their turn come under my protection and guarantee, I will not lighten my hand from off them.'

"This they did at once. Now," said Fergus in conclusion. "I submit that a youngster who did all this when he was just five years old needs not to excite our wonder, because, now being turned of seventeen years, he in this Cattle-Raid of Cooley cut a four-pronged pole and the rest, and that he should have killed a man, or two, or three men, or even—as indeed he has done—four."

9th CENTURY

The Kildare Pooka

BY PATRICK KENNEDY

mr. H———R———, when he was alive, used to live a good deal in Dublin, and he was once a great while out of the country on account of the "ninety-eight" business. But the servants kept on in the big house at Rath——— all the same as if the family was at home. Well, they used to be frightened out of their lives after going to their beds, with the banging of the kitchen door, and the clattering of fire-irons, and the pots and plates and dishes.

One evening they sat up ever so long, keeping one another in heart with telling stories about ghosts and fetches, and that when—what would you have of it?—the little scullery boy, who used to be sleeping over the horses, and could not get room at the fire, crept into the hot hearth, and when he got tired listening to the stories, sorra fear him, but he fell dead asleep.

Well and good, after they were all gone and the kitchen fire raked up, the boy was woke with the noise of the kitchen door opening, and the trampling of an ass on the kitchen floor. He peeped out, and what should he see but a big ass, sure enough, sitting on his curabingo and yawning before the fire. After a little the ass looked about him, and began scratching his ears as if he was quite tired, and says he, "I may as well begin first as last."

The poor boy's teeth began to chatter in his head, for says he, "Now he's goin' to ate me."

But the fellow with long ears and tail on him had something else to do. He stirred the fire, and then he brought in a pail of water from the pump and filled a big pot that he put on the fire before he went out. He then put his hand—foot, I mean—into the hot hearth, and pulled out the little boy, who let a roar out of him with the fright. But the pooka only looked at him, and thrust out his lower lip to show how little he valued him, and then he pitched him into his pew again.

Well, the Pooka then lay down before the fire till he heard the boil coming on the water, and maybe there wasn't a plate, or a dish, or a spoon on the dresser that he didn't fetch and put into the pot, and wash and dry the whole bilin' of 'em as well as e'er a kitchen-maid from that to Dublin town. He put all of them up in their places on the shelves; and if he didn't give a good sweepin' to the kitchen, leave it till again.

Then he comes and sits fornent the boy, let down one of his ears, and cocked up the other, and gave a grin. The poor fellow strove to roar out, but not a dheeg 'ud come out of his throat. The last thing the pooka done was to rake up the fire, and walk out, giving such a slap o' the door, that the boy thought the house couldn't help tumbling down.

Well, to be sure if there wasn't a hullabaloo next morning when the poor fellow told his story! They could talk of nothing else the whole day. One said one thing, another said another, but a fat, lazy scullery girl said the wittiest thing of all. "Musha!" says she, "If the pooka does be cleaning up everything that way when we are asleep, what should we be slaving ourselves for doing his work?"

"Shu gu dheine," says another, "them's the wisest words you ever said, Kauth. It's meeself won't contradict you." So said, so done. Not a bit of a plate or dish saw a drop of water that evening, and not a besom was laid on the floor and everyone went to bed soon after sundown.

Next morning everything was as fine as fine in the kitchen, and the lord mayor might eat his dinner off the flags. It was great ease to the lazy servants, you may depend, and everything went on well till a fool-hardy gag of a boy said he would stay up one night and have a chat with the pooka.

He was a little daunted when the door was thrown open and the ass marched up to the fire.

"And then, sir," says he, at last, picking up courage, "if it isn't taking a liberty, might I ax who you are, and why you are so kind as to do half of the day's work for the girls every night?"

"No liberty at all," says the pooka, says he. "I'll tell you, and welcome. I was a servant in the time of Squire R———'s father, and was the laziest rogue that ever was clothed and fed, and done nothing for it. When my time came for the other world, this is the punishment was laid on me—to come here and do all this labour every night, and then go out in the cold. It isn't so bad in the fine weather: but if you only knew what it is to stand with

30

your head between your legs, facing the storm, from midnight to sunrise, on a bleak winter night."

"And could we do anything for your comfort, my poor fellow?" says the boy.

"Musha, I don't know," says the pooka. "But I think a good quilted frieze coat would help to keep the life in me them cold long nights."

"Why then, in troth, we'd be the ungratefullest of people if we didn't feel for you."

To make a long story short, the next night but two the boy was there again and if he didn't delight the poor pooka, holding up a fine warm coat before him, it's no mather! Betune the pooka and the man, his legs was got into the four arms of it, and it was buttoned down the breast and the belly, and he was so pleased he walked up to the glass to see how he looked.

"Well," says he, "it's a long lane that has no turning. I am much obliged to you and your fellow-servants. You have made me happy at last. Goodnight to you."

So he was walking out, but the other cried: "Och, sure you're going too soon! What about the washing and sweeping?"

"Ah, you may tell the girls that they must now get their turn. My punishment was to last till I was thought worthy of a reward for the way I'd done my duty. You'll see me no more."

And no more they did, and right sorry they were for having been in such a hurry to reward the ungrateful pooka.

How Cormac MacArt went to Faery

BY JOSEPH JACOBS

Cormac, son of Art, son of Conn of the Hundred Battles, was High King of Ireland, and held his Court at Tara. One day he saw a youth upon the green having in his hand a glittering faery branch with nine apples of red. And whensoever the branch was shaken, wounded men and women enfeebled by illness would be lulled to sleep by the sound of the very sweet faery music which those apples uttered; nor could anyone upon earth bear in mind any want, woe or weariness of soul when the branch was shaken for him.

"Is that branch thy own?" said Cormac.

"It is indeed mine."

"Wouldst thou sell it? And what wouldst thou require for it?"

"Will you give me what I ask?" said the youth.

The King promised, and the youth then claimed his wife, his daughter and his son. Sorrowful of heart was the King, heaviness of heart filled his wife and children when they learned that they must part from him. But Cormac shook the branch amongst them, and when they heard the soft, sweet music of the branch they forgot all care and sorrow and went forth to meet the youth, and he and they took their departure and were seen no more.

Loud cries of weeping and mourning were made throughout Erin when this was known, but Cormac shook the branch so that there was no longer any grief or heaviness of heart upon anyone.

After a year Cormac said: "It is a year today since my wife, my son, and my daughter were taken from me. I will follow them by the same path that they took."

Cormac went off, and a dark magical mist rose about him, and he chanced to come upon a wonderful, marvellous plain. Many

33

horsemen were there, busy thatching a house with the feathers of foreign birds. When one side was thatched they would go and seek more, and when they returned, not a feather was on the roof. Cormac gazed at them for a while and then went forward.

Again, he saw a youth dragging up trees to make a fire, but before he could find a second tree the first one would be burnt, and it seemed to Cormac that his labour would never end.

Cormac journeyed onwards until he saw three immense wells on the border of the plain, and on each well was a head. From out of the mouth of the first head there flowed two streams, into it there flowed one. The second head had a stream flowing out of and another stream into its mouth, whilst three streams were flowing from the mouth of the third head.

Great wonder seized Cormac, and he said: "I will stay and gaze upon these wells, for I should find no man to tell me their story."

With that he set onwards till he came to a house in the middle of a field. He entered and greeted the inmates. There sat within a tall couple clad in many-hued garments, and they greeted the King, and bade him welcome for the night.

Then the wife bade her husband seek food, and he arose and returned with a huge wild boar upon his back and a log in his hand. He cast down the swine and the log upon the floor, and said: "There is meat; cook it yourselves."

"How can I do that?" said Cormac.

"I will teach you," said the man. "Split this great log, make four pieces of it, and make four quarters of the hog. Put a log under each quarter, tell a true story, and the meat will be cooked."

"Tell the first story yourself," said Cormac.

"Seven pigs I have of the same kind as the one I bought, and I could feed the world with them. For if a pig is killed I have but to put its bones into the sty again, and it will be found alive the next morning."

The story was true, and a quarter of the pig was cooked.

Then Cormac begged the woman of the house to tell a story.

"I have seven white cows, and they fill seven cauldrons with milk every day, and I give my word that they yield as much milk as would satisfy the men of the whole world if they were out on yonder plain drinking it."

The story was true, and a second quarter of the pig was cooked.

Cormac was bidden now to tell a story for his quarter, and he told how he was upon a search for his wife, his son and his

daughter that had been borne away from him a year before by a youth with a faery branch.

"If what thou sayest be true," said the man of the house, "thou art indeed Cormac, son of Art, son of Conn of the Hundred Battles."

"Truly I am," quoth Cormac.

That story was true, and a quarter of the pig was cooked.

"Eat thy meal now," said the man of the house.

"I never ate before," said Cormac, "having only two people in my company."

"Wouldst thou eat it with three others?"

"If they were dear to me, I would," said Cormac.

The door opened, and there entered the wife and children of Cormac. Great was his joy and his exultation.

Then Manannan mac Lir, lord of the faery cavalcade, appeared before him in his own true form, and said thus: "I it was, Cormac, who bore away these three from thee. I it was who gave thee this branch, all that I might bring thee here. Eat now and drink."

"I would do so," said Cormac, "could I learn the meaning of the wonders I saw today."

"Thou shalt learn them," said Manannan. "The horsemen thatching the roof with feathers are a likeness of people who go forth into the world to seek riches and fortune. When they return their houses are bare, and so they go on for ever.

"The young man dragging up the trees to make a fire is a likeness of those who labour for others: much trouble they have, but they never warm themselves at the fire.

"The three heads in the wells are three kinds of men. Some there are who give freely when they get freely; some who give freely though they get little; some who get much and give little— and they are the worst of the three, Cormac," said Manannan.

After that Cormac and his wife and his children sat down, and a tablecloth was spread before them.

"That is a very precious thing before thee," said Manannan. "There is no food however delicate that shall be asked of it but it shall be had without doubt."

"That is well," quoth Cormac.

After that Manannan thrust his hand into his girdle and brought out a goblet and set it upon his palm.

"This cup has this virtue," said he, "that when a false story is told before it, it makes four pieces of it, and when a true story is related it is made whole again."

"Those are very precious things you have, Manannan," said the King.

"They shall all be thine," said Manannan. "The goblet, the branch and the tablecloth."

Then they ate their meal, and that meal was good, for they had only to think of any meat and they got it upon the tablecloth, and any drink, which they got in the cup. Great thanks did they give to Manannan.

When they had eaten their meal, a couch was prepared for them and they laid down to slumber and sweet sleep. Where they rose on the morrow morn was in Tara of the Kings, and by their side were tablecloth, cup and branch.

Thus did Cormac fare at the Court of Manannan, and this is how he got the faery branch.

The Brewery of Egg-shells

BY T. CROFTON CROKER

I t might be considered impertinent were I to explain what is meant by a changeling. Both Shakespeare and Spenser have already done so, and who is there unacquainted with *A Midsummer Night's Dream* and *The Faerie Queene*?

Now Mrs. Sullivan fancied that her youngest child had been exchanged by "fairies' theft", and certainly appearances warranted such a conclusion; for in one night her healthy, blue-eyed boy had become shrivelled up into almost nothing, and never ceased squalling and crying. This naturally made poor Mrs. Sullivan very unhappy and all the neighbours, by way of comforting her, said that her own child was, beyond any kind of doubt, with the good people, and that one of themselves was put in his place.

Mrs. Sullivan of course could not disbelieve what everyone told her, but she did not wish to hurt the thing. For although its face was so withered, and its body wasted away to a mere skeleton, it had still a strong resemblance of her own boy. She therefore could not find it in her heart to roast it alive on the griddle, or to burn its nose off with the red-hot tongs, or to throw it out in the snow on the roadside—notwithstanding these, and several like proceedings, were strongly recommended to her for the recovery of her child.

One day who should Mrs. Sullivan meet but a cunning woman, well known about the country by the name of Ellen Leah (or Grey Ellen). She had a gift, however she got it, of telling where the dead were, and what was good for the rest of their souls. She could charm away warts and wens, and do a great many wonderful things of the same nature.

"You're in grief this morning, Mrs. Sullivan," were the first words of Ellen Leah to her.

"You may say that, Ellen," said Mrs. Sullivan, "and good cause I have to be in grief. For there was my own fine child whipped off from me out of his cradle, without as much as 'by your leave' or 'ask your pardon,' and an ugly dony [tiny] bit of a shrivelled-up fairy put in his place. No wonder then that you see me in grief, Ellen."

"Small blame to you, Mrs. Sullivan," said Ellen Leah. "But are you sure 'tis a fairy?"

"Sure?" echoed Mrs. Sullivan. "Sure enough I am to my sorrow, and can I doubt my own two eyes? Every mother's soul must feel for me!"

"Will you take an old woman's advice?" said Ellen Leah, fixing her wild and mysterious gaze upon the unhappy mother. After a pause, she added, "but maybe you'll call it foolish?"

"Can you get me back my child, my own child, Ellen?" said Mrs. Sullivan with great energy.

"If you do as I bid you," returned Ellen Leah, "you'll know." Mrs. Sullivan was silent in expectation, and Ellen continued: "Put down a big pot, full of water, on the fire, and make it boil like mad; then get a dozen new-laid eggs, break them, and keep the shells, but throw away the rest; when that is done, put the shells in the pot of boiling water, and you will soon know whether it is your own boy or a fairy. If you find that it is a fairy in the cradle, take the red-hot poker and cram it down his ugly throat, and you will not have much trouble with him after that, I promise you."

Home went Mrs. Sullivan, and did as Ellen Leah desired. She put the pot on the fire, and plenty of turf under it, and set the water boiling at such a pace, that if ever water was red-hot, it surely was.

The child was lying, for a wonder, quite easy and quiet in the cradle, every now and then cocking his eye, that would twinkle as keen as a star in a frosty night, over at the great fire, and the big pot upon it. And he looked on with great attention at Mrs. Sullivan breaking the eggs and putting down the egg-shells to boil. At last he asked, with the voice of a very old man, "What are you doing, Mammy?"

Mrs. Sullivan's heart, as she said herself, was up in her mouth ready to choke her, at hearing the child speak. But she contrived to put the poker in the fire, and to answer without making any wonder at the words, "I'm brewing, a vick [my son]."

"And what are you brewing, Mammy?" said the little imp, whose supernatural gift of speech now proved beyond question that he was a fairy substitute.

"I wish the poker was red," thought Mrs. Sullivan; but it was a large one, and took a long time heating. So she determined to keep him in talk until the poker was in a proper state to thrust down his throat, and therefore repeated the question.

"Is it what I'm brewing, a vick," said she, "you want to know?"

"Yes, Mammy. What are you brewing?" returned the fairy.

"Egg-shells, a vick," said Mrs. Sullivan.

"Oh!" shrieked the imp, starting up in the cradle and clapping his hands together. "I'm fifteen hundred years in the world, and I never saw a brewery of egg-shells before!"

The poker was by this time quite red and Mrs. Sullivan, seizing it, ran furiously towards the cradle. But somehow or other her foot slipped, and she fell flat on the floor, and the poker flew out of her hand to the other end of the house.

However, she got up without much loss of time and went to the cradle, intending to pitch the wicked thing that was in it into the pot of boiling water. But there she saw her own child in a sweet sleep, one of his soft round arms rested upon the pillow; his features were as placid as if their repose had never been disturbed, save the rosy mouth, which moved with a gentle and regular breathing.

Who can tell the feelings of a mother when she looks upon her sleeping child? Why should I therefore endeavour to describe those of Mrs. Sullivan at again beholding her long-lost boy? The fountains of her heart overflowed with the excess of joy, and she wept. Tears trickled silently down her cheek, nor did she strive to stop them—they were tears, not of sorrow, but of happiness.

The Story of Deirdre

BY JOSEPH JACOBS

here was a man in Ireland once who was called Malcolm Harper. The man was a right good man, and he had a goodly share of this world's goods. He had a wife, but no family. What did Malcolm hear but that a soothsayer had come home to the place, and as the man was a right good man, he wished that the soothsayer might come near them. Whether it was that he was invited or that he came of himself, the soothsayer came to the house of Malcolm.

"Are you doing any soothsaying?" says Malcolm.

"Yes, I am doing a little. Are you in need of soothsaying?"

"Well, I do not mind taking soothsaying from you, if you have soothsaying for me, and you would be willing to do it."

"Well, I will do soothsaying for you. What kind of soothsaying do you want?"

"Well, the soothsaying I wanted was that you would tell me my lot or what will happen to me, if you can give me knowledge of it."

"Well, I am going out, and when I return, I will tell you."

And the soothsayer went forth out of the house and he was not long outside when he returned.

"Well," said the soothsayer, "I saw in my second sight that on account of a daughter of yours the greatest amount of blood shall be shed that has ever been shed in Erin since time and race began. And the three most famous heroes that ever were found will lose their heads on her account."

After a time a daughter was born to Malcolm, and because of the soothsaying he did not allow a living being to come to his house, only himself and the nurse, He asked this woman: "Will you yourself bring up the child to keep her in hiding far away,

43

where eye will not see a sight of her nor ear hear a word about her!"

The woman said she would, so Malcolm got three men, and he took them away to a large mountain, distant and far from reach, without the knowledge or notice of anyone. He caused there a hillock, round and green, to be dug out of the middle, and the hole thus made to be covered carefully over so that a little company could dwell there together. This was done.

Deirdre and her foster-mother dwelt in the bothy mid the hills without the knowledge or the suspicion of any living person about them and without anything occurring, until Deirdre was sixteen years of age. Deirdre grew like the white sapling, straight and trim as the rash on the moss. She was the creature of fairest form, of loveliest aspect, and of gentlest nature that existed between earth and heaven in all Ireland; and whatever colour of hue she had before, there was nobody that looked into her face but she would blush fiery red over it.

The woman who had charge of her gave Deirdre every information and skill of which she herself had knowledge and skill. There was not a blade of grass growing from root, nor a bird singing in the wood, nor a star shining from heaven but Deirdre had a name for it. Yet one thing the woman did not wish her to have either part or parley with—any single living man of the rest of the world.

But on a gloomy winter night, with black, scowling clouds, a hunter of game was wearily travelling the hills, and what happened but that he missed the trail of the hunt, and lost his course and companions. A drowsiness came upon the man as he wearily wandered over the hills, faint from hunger and wandering, and benumbed with cold. When at last he lay down beside the green hill in which Deirdre lived, a deep sleep fell upon him and a troubled dream came to him. He thought that he enjoyed the warmth of a fairy broch, the fairies being inside playing music. The hunter shouted out in his dream, if there was anyone in the broch, to let him in for the Holy One's sake.

Deirdre heard the voice and said to her foster-mother: "O foster-mother, what cry is that?"

"It is nothing at all, Deirdre, merely the birds of the air astray and seeking each other. But let them go past to the bosky glade. There is no shelter or house for them here."

"Oh, foster-mother, the bird asked to get inside for the sake of God of the Elements, and you yourself tell me that anything that is asked in His name we ought to do. If you will not allow the bird that is being benumbed with cold, and done to death with hunger, to be let in, I do not think much of your language or your faith. But since I give credence to your language and to your faith, which you taught me, I will myself let in the bird."

Deirdre arose and drew the bolt from the leaf of the door, and she let in the hunter. She placed a seat in the place for sitting, food in the place for eating, and drink in the place for drinking for the man who came to the house.

"Oh, for this life and raiment, you man that came in, keep restraint on your tongue!" said the old woman. "It is not a great thing for you to keep your mouth shut and your tongue quiet when you get a home and shelter of a hearth on a gloomy winter's night."

"Well," said the hunter, "I may do that—keep my mouth shut and my tongue quiet, since I came to the house and received hospitality from you. But by the hand of thy father and grandfather, and by your own two hands, if some other of the people of the world saw this beauteous creature you have here hid away, they would not long leave her with you, I swear."

"What men are these you refer to?" said Deirdre.

"Well, I will tell you, young woman," said the hunter. "They are Naois, son of Uisnech, and Allen and Arden his two brothers."

"What like are these men when seen, if we were to see them?" said Deirdre.

"Why, the aspect and form of the men when seen are these," said the hunter. "They have the colour of the raven on their hair, their skin like swan on the wave in whiteness, and their cheeks as the blood of the brindled red calf, and their speed and their leap are those of the salmon of the torrent and the deer of the grey mountainside. And Naois is head and shoulder over the rest of the people of Erin."

"However they are," said the nurse, "be you off from here and take another road. And, King of Light and Sun, in good sooth and certainty, little are my thanks for yourself or for her that let you in!"

The hunter went away, and went straight to the palace of King Connachar. He sent word in to the King that he wished to speak to him if he pleased. The King answered the message and came out to speak to the man. "What is the reason of your journey?" said the King to the hunter.

"I have only to tell you, O King," said the hunter, "that I saw the fairest creature that ever was born in Erin, and I came to tell you of it."

"Who is this beauty and where is she to be seen, when she was not seen before till you saw her, if you did see her?"

"Well, I did see her," said the hunter, "But, if I did, no man else can see her unless he gets directions from me as to where she is dwelling."

"And will you direct me to where she dwells? And the reward of your directing me will be as good as the reward of your message," said the King.

"Well, I will direct you, O King, although it is likely that this will not be what they want," said the hunter.

Connachar, King of Ulster, sent for his nearest kinsmen, and he told them of his intent. Though early rose the song of the birds mid the rocky caves and the music of the birds in the grove, earlier than that did Connachar, King of Ulster, arise, with his little troop of dear friends, in the delightful twilight of the fresh and gentle May. The dew was heavy on each bush and flower and stem, as they went to bring Deirdre forth from the green knoll where she stayed. Many a youth was there who had a lithe, leaping and lissom step when they started, whose step was faint, failing, and faltering when they reached the bothy on account of the length of the way and roughness of the road.

"Yonder now, down in the bottom of the glen, is the bothy where the woman dwells, but I will not go nearer than this to the old woman," said the hunter.

Connachar with his band of kinsfolk went down to the green knoll where Deirdre dwelt and he knocked at the door of the bothy. The nurse replied: "No less than a King's command and a King's army could put me out of my bothy tonight. And I should be obliged to you, were you to tell who it is that wants me to open my bothy door."

"It is I, Connachar, King of Ulster."

When the poor woman heard who was at the door, she rose with haste and let in the King and all that could get in of his retinue.

When the King saw the woman that was before him that he had been in quest of, he thought he never saw in the course of the day nor in the dream of night a creature so fair as Deirdre and he gave his full heart's weight of love to her. Deirdre was raised on the topmost of the heroes' shoulders and she and her foster-mother were brought to the Court of King Connachar of Ulster.

With the love that Connachar had for her, he wanted to marry Deirdre right off there and then, will she nill she marry him. But she said to him: "I would be obliged to you if you will give me the respite of a year and day."

He said: "I will grant you that, hard though it is, if you will give me your unfailing promise that you will marry me at the year's end." And she gave the promise.

Connachar got for her a woman-teacher and merry modest maidens fair that would lie down and rise with her, that would play and speak with her. Deirdre was clever in maidenly duties and wifely understanding, and Connachar thought he never saw with bodily eye a creature that pleased him more.

Deirdre and her women companions were one day out on the hillock behind the house enjoying the scene, and drinking in the sun's heat. What did they see coming but three men a-journeying? Deirdre was looking at the men that were coming, and wondering at them. When the men neared them, Deirdre remembered the language of the huntsman, and she said to herself that these were the three sons of Uisnech, and that this was Naois, he having what was above the bend of the two shoulders above the men of Erin all.

The three brothers went past without taking any notice of them, without even glancing at the young girls on the hillock. What happened but that love for Naois struck the heart of Deirdre, so that she could not but follow after him. She girded up her raiment and went after the men that went past the base of the knoll, leaving her women attendants there.

Allen and Arden had heard of the woman that Connachar, King of Ulster, had with him, and they thought that if Naois, their brother, saw her, he would have her himself, more especially as she was not married to the King. They perceived the woman coming, and called on one another to hasten their step as they had a long distance to travel, and the dusk of night was coming on. They did so.

She cried: "Naois, son of Uisnech, will you leave me?"

"What piercing, shrill cry is that—the most melodious my ear ever heard, and the shrillest that ever struck my heart of all the cries I ever heard?"

"Is it anything else but the wail of the wave-swans of Connachar?" said his brothers.

"No! Yonder is a woman's cry of distress," said Naois, and he swore he would not go farther until he saw from whom the cry came, and Naois turned back.

Naois and Deirdre met, and Deirdre kissed Naois three times, and a kiss each to his brothers. With the confusion that she was in, Deirdre went into a crimson blaze of fire, and her colour came and went as rapidly as the movement of the aspen by the stream side. Naois thought he never saw a fairer creature, and Naois gave Deirdre the love that he never gave to thing, to vision, or to creature but to herself. Then Naois placed Deirdre on the topmost height of his shoulder, and told his brothers to keep up their pace, and they kept up their pace.

Naois thought that it would not be well for him to remain in Erin on account of the way in which Connachar, King of Ulster, his kinsman, would go against him because of Deirdre, though he had not married her; and he turned back to Alba—that is, Scotland. He reached the side of Loch Ness and made his habitation there. He could kill the salmon of the torrent from out his own door, and the deer of the grey gorge out his window. Naois and Deirdre and Allen and Arden dwelt in a tower, and they were happy so long a time as they were there.

By this time the end of the period came when Deirdre had to marry Connachar, King of Ulster. Connachar made up his mind to take Deirdre away by the sword whether she was married to Naois or not. So he prepared a great and gleeful feast. He sent word far and wide through Erin all to his kinspeople to come to the feast. Connachar thought to himself that Naois would not come, though he should bid him; and the scheme that arose in his mind was to send for his father's brother, Ferchar Mac Ro, and to send him on an embassy to Naois.

He did so, and Connachar said to Ferchar: "Tell Naois, son of Uisnech, that I am setting forth a great and gleeful feast to my friends and kinspeople throughout the wide extent of Erin all, and that I shall not have rest by day nor sleep by night if he and Allen and Arden be not partakers of the feast."

Ferchar Mac Ro and his three sons went on their journey, and reached the tower where Naois was dwelling by the side of Loch Ness. The sons of Uisnech gave a cordial kindly welcome to Ferchar Mac Ro and his three sons, and asked of him the news of Erin.

"The best news that I have for you," said the hardy hero, "is that Connachar, King of Ulster, is setting forth a great sumptuous feast to his friends and kinspeople throughout the wide extent of Erin all, and he has vowed by the earth beneath him, by the high heaven above him, and by the sun that wends to the west, that he will have no rest by day nor sleep by night if the sons of Uisnech, the sons of his own father's brother, will not come back to the land of their home and the soil of their nativity, and to the feast likewise, and he has sent us on embassy to invite you."

"We will go with you," said Naois.

"We will," said his brothers.

But Deirdre did not wish to go with Ferchar Mac Ro, and she tried every prayer to turn Naois from going with him, She said: "I saw a vision, Naois, and do you interpret it to me." Then she sang:

> O Naois, son of Uisnech, hear
> What was shown in a dream to me.

> There came three white doves out of the South,
> Flying over the sea,
> And drops of honey were in their mouth
> From the hive of the honey-bee.

> O Naois, son of Uisnech, hear
> What was shown in a dream to me.

> I saw three grey hawks out of the south
> Come flying over the sea,
> And the red red drops they bare in their mouth
> They were dearer than life to me.

Said Naois:

> It is nought but the fear of woman's heart,
> And a dream of the night, Deirdre.

"The day that Connachar sent the invitation to his feast will be unlucky for us if we don't go, O Deirdre," said Naois.

"You will go there," said Ferchar Mac Ro. "And if Connachar show kindness to you, show ye kindness to him; and if he will display wrath towards you, display ye wrath towards him, and I and my three sons will be with you."

49

"We will," said Daring Drop.

"We will," said Hardy Holly.

"We will," said Fiallan the Fair.

"I have three sons, and they are three heroes, and in any harm or danger that may befall you, they will be with you, and I myself will be along with them." And Ferchar Mac Ro gave his vow and his word in presence of his arms that, if any harm or danger came in the way of the sons of Uisnech, he and his three sons would not leave head on live body in Erin, despite sword or helmet, spear or shield, blade or mail, be they ever so good.

Deirdre was unwilling to leave Alba, but she went with Naois. Deirdre wept tears in showers and she sang:

> Dear is the land, the land over there,
>   Alba full of woods and lakes;
> Bitter to my heart is leaving thee,
>   But I go away with Naois.

Ferchar Mac Ro did not stop till he got the sons of Uisnech away with him, despite the suspicion of Deirdre.

> The coracle was put to sea,
>   The sail was hoisted to it;
> And the second morrow they arrived
>   On the white shores of Erin.

As soon as the sons of Uisnech landed in Erin, Ferchar Mac Ro sent word to Connachar, King of Ulster, that the men whom he wanted were come, and let him now show kindness to them.

"Well," said Connachar, "I did not expect that the sons of Uisnech would come, though I sent for them, and I am not quite ready to receive them. But there is a house down yonder where I keep strangers, and let them go down to it today, and my house will be ready for them tomorrow."

But he that was up in the palace felt it long that he was not getting word as to how matters were going on for those down in the house of the strangers.

"Go you, Gelban Grednach, son of Lochlin's King, go you down and bring me information as to whether her former hue and complexion are on Deirdre. If they be, I will take her out with edge of blade and point of sword, and if not, let Naois, son of Uisnech, have her for himself," said Connacher.

Gelban, the cheering and charming son of Lochlin's King, went down to the place of the strangers, where the sons of Uisnech and Deirdre were staying. He looked in through the bicker-hole on the door-leaf. Now she that he gazed upon used to go into a crimson blaze of blushes when anyone looked at her. Naois looked at Deirdre and knew that someone was looking at her from the back of the door-leaf. He seized one of the dice on the table before him and fired it through the bicker-hole, and knocked the eye out of Gelban Grednach the Cheerful and Charming, right through the back of his head. Gelban returned back to the palace of King Connacher.

"You were cheerful, charming, going away, but you are cheerless, charmless, returning. What has happened to you, Gelban? But have you seen her, and are Deirdre's hue and complexion as before?" said Connachar.

"Well, I have seen Deirdre, and I saw her also truly, and while I was looking at her through the bicker-hole on the door, Naois, son of Uisnech, knocked out my eye with one of the dice in his hand. But of a truth and verity, although he put out even my eye, it were my desire still to remain looking at her with the other eye, were it not for the hurry you told me to be in," said Gelban.

Connachar ordered three hundred active heroes to go down to the abode of the strangers and to take Deirdre up with them and kill the rest.

"The pursuit is coming," said Deirdre.

"Yes, but I will myself go out and stop the pursuit," said Naois.

"It is not you, but we that will go," said Daring Drop, and Hardy Holly, and Fiallan the Fair. "It is to us that our father entrusted your defence from harm and danger when he himself left for home."

And the gallant youths, full noble, full manly, full handsome, with beauteous brown locks, went forth girt with battle arms fit for fierce fight and clothed for fierce contest with combat dress which was burnished bright, brilliant, bladed, blazing, on which were many pictures of beasts and birds and creeping things, lions and lithe-limbed tigers, brown eagle and harrying hawk and adder fierce; and the young heroes laid low three-thirds of the company.

Connachar came out in haste and cried with wrath: "Who is there on the floor of fight, slaughtering my men?"

"We, the three sons of Ferchar Mac Ro."

"Well," said the King, "I will give a free bridge to your grandfather, a free bridge to your father, and a free bridge each to you three brothers, if you come over to my side tonight."

"Well, Connachar, we will not accept that offer from you, nor thank you for it. Greater by far do we prefer to go home to our father and tell the deeds of heroism we have done, than accept anything on these terms from you. Naois, son of Uisnech, and Allen and Arden are as nearly related to yourself as they are to us, though you are so keen to shed their blood, and you shed our blood also, Connachar."

And the noble, manly, handsome youths with beauteous brown locks returned inside. "We are now," said they, "going home to tell our father that you are now safe from the hands of the King."

And the youths all fresh and tall and lithe and beautiful, went home to their father to tell that the sons of Uisnech were safe. This happened at the parting of the day and night in the morning twilight time.

And Naois said they must go away, leave that house, and return to Alba. So Naois and Deirdre, Allen and Arden started to return to Alba.

But word came to the King that the company he was in pursuit of were gone. The King then sent for Duanan Gacha Druid, the best magician he had, and he spoke to him as follows: "Too much wealth have I expended on you, Duanan Gacha Druid, to give schooling and learning and magic mystery to you, if these people get away from me today without care, without consideration or regard for me, without chance of overtaking them, and without power to stop them."

"Well, I will stop them," said the magician, "until the company you send in pursuit return." And the magician placed a wood before them through which no man could go, but the sons of Uisnech marched through the wood without halt or hesitation, and Deirdre held on to Naois's hand.

"What is the good of that? That will not do yet," said Connachar. "They are off without bending of their feet or stopping of their step, without heed or respect to me, and I am without power to keep up to them or opportunity to turn them back this night."

"I will try another plan on them," said the druid, and he placed before them a grey sea instead of a green plain. The three heroes stripped and tied their clothes behind their heads, and Naois placed Deirdre on the top of his shoulder.

They stretched their sides to the stream,
  And sea and land were to them the same;
The rough grey ocean was the same
  As meadow-land green and plain.

"Though that be good, O Duanan, it will not make the heroes return," said Connachar. "They are gone without regard for me, and without honour to me, and without power on my part to pursue them or to force them to return this night."

"We shall try another method on them, since yon one did not stop them," said the druid. And the druid froze the grey-ridged sea into hardy rocky knobs, the sharpness of sword being on the one edge and the poison power of adders on the other.

Then Arden cried that he was getting tired, and nearly giving over. "Come you, Arden, and sit on my right shoulder," said Naois. Arden came and sat on Naois's shoulder. Arden was long in this posture when he died; but though he was dead Naois would not let him go.

Allen then cried out that he was getting faint and nigh-well giving up, and he gave forth the piercing sigh of death. But Naois heard his cry and asked Allen to lay hold of him and he would bring him to land.

Allen was not long when the weakness of death came on him and his hold failed. Naois looked around, and when he saw his two well-beloved brothers dead, he cared not whether he lived or died, and he gave forth the bitter sigh of death, and his heart burst.

"They are gone," said Duanan Gacha Druid to the King, "and I have done what you desired me. The sons of Uisnech are dead and they will trouble you no more; and you have your wife hale and whole to yourself."

"Blessings for that upon you and may the good results accrue to me, Duanan. I count it no loss what I spent in the schooling and teaching of you. Now dry up the flood, and let me see if I can behold Deirdre," said Connachar.

And Duanan Gacha Druid dried up the flood from the plain and the three sons of Uisnech were lying together dead, without breath of life, side by side on the green meadow plain and Deirdre bending above showering down her tears.

Then Deirdre said this lament: "Fair one, loved one, flower of beauty, beloved upright and strong, beloved noble and modest warrior. Fair one, blue-eyed, beloved of thy wife, lovely to me

at the trysting-place came thy clear voice through the woods of Ireland. I cannot eat or smile henceforth. Break not today, my heart. Soon enough shall I lie within my grave. Strong are the waves of sorrow, but stronger is sorrow's self, Connachar."

The people then gathered round the heroes' bodies and asked Connachar what was to be done with the bodies. The order that he gave was that they should dig a pit and put the three brothers in it side by side.

Deirdre kept sitting on the brink of the grave, constantly asking the gravediggers to dig the pit wide and free. When the bodies of the brothers were put in the grave, Deirdre said:

> Come over hither, Naois, my love,
>   Let Arden close to Allen lie;
> If the dead had any sense to feel,
>   Ye would have made a place for Deirdre.

The men did as she told them. She jumped into the grave and lay down by Naois, and she was dead by his side.

The King ordered the body to be raised from out the grave and to be buried on the other side of the loch. It was done as the King bade, and the pit closed. Thereupon a fir shoot grew out of the grave of Deirdre and a fir shoot from the grave of Naois, and the two shoots united in a knot above the loch. The King ordered the shoots to be cut down, and this was done twice, until, at the third time, the wife whom the King had married caused him to stop this work of evil and his vengeance on the remains of the dead.

How the Shannon Acquired its Name

BY PATRICK KENNEDY

a long time ago there was a well in Ossory, shaded by a rowan tree. When the berries became ripe they would drop into the water, and be eaten by the salmon that had their residence in the well. Red spots would then appear on the fish, and they received the name of "Salmon of Knowledge". It was not so easy to take these salmon, for there were shelving banks, and they could also retreat into the cavern from which the waters issued that supplied the well.

However, one was occasionally caught, and the captor, as soon as he had made his repast on it, found himself gifted with extraordinary knowledge, even as Fion, son of Cumhail, when he had tasted of the broiled salmon of the Boyne.

It was understood that no woman could taste of this delicacy and live. Yet Sionan, a lady cursed with an extraordinary desire of knowledge, braved the danger, suspecting the report to be spread abroad and maintained by the male sex from merely selfish motives. So, in order to lose no time, she had a fire ready by the side of the well, and the unfortunate fish was scarcely flung out on the grass when he was frying on the coals.

Who can describe the rapture she felt from the burst of light that filled her mind on swallowing the first morsel! Alas—the next moment she was enveloped by the furious waters, which, bursting forth, swept westwards, and carried the unfortunate lady with them till they were lost in the great river which ever after bore her name.

The King and the Bishop

BY SAMUEL LOVER

Samuel Lover in his travels visits the ruined abbey of Clonmacnoise.

One day I was accosted by a peasant who had watched for a long time, in silent wonder, the draft of the stone cross, as it grew into being beneath my pencil; and finding the man apt, as the ghost says to Hamlet, I entered into conversation with him. To some remark of mine touching the antiquity of the place, he assured me "it was a fine ould place, in the ould ancient times". In noticing the difference between the two round towers—for there are two very fine ones at Clonmacnoise, one on the top of the hill, and one close beside the plashy bank of the river—he accounted for the difference by a piece of legendary information with which he favoured me and which may, perhaps, prove of sufficient importance to interest the reader.

"You see, sir," said he, "the one down there beyant, at the river side, was built the first, and finished complate entirely, for the roof is an it, you see. But when that was built, the bishop thought that another id look very purty on the hill beyant, and so he bid the masons set to work, and build up another tower there.

"Well, away they went to work, as busy as nailers; troth it was jist like a bee-hive, every man with his hammer in his hand, and sure the tower was complated in due time.

"Well, when the last stone was laid on the roof, the bishop axes the masons how much he was to pay them, and they ups and towld him their price. But the bishop, they say, was a neygar [niggard]—God forgi' me for saying the word of so holy a man!—and he said they axed too much, and he wouldn't pay them. With that, my jew'l, the masons said they would take no less; and what would you think, but the bishop had the cunnin' to take away the ladthers that was reared up agin the tower.

" 'And now,' says he, 'my gay fellows,' says he, 'the divil a down out o' that you'll come antil you larn manners, and take what's offered to yees,' says he. 'And when yees come down in your price you may come down yourselves into the bargain.'

"Well, sure enough, he kep his word, and wouldn't let man nor mortyel go nigh them to help them. And faiks, the masons didn't like the notion of losing their honest airnins, and small blame to them. But sure they wor starvin' all the same and didn't know what in the wide world to do, when there was a fool chanced to pass by, and seen them.

" 'Musha! but you look well there,' says the innocent. 'An' how are you?' says he.

" 'Not much the betther av your axin,' says they.

" 'Maybe you're out there,' says he. So he questioned them, and they tould him how it was with them, and how the bishop tuk away the ladthers, and they couldn't come down.

" 'Tut, you fools,' says he. 'Sure isn't it asier to take down two stones nor to put up one?'

"Wasn't that mighty cute o' the fool, sir? And wid that, my dear sowl, no sooner said than done. Faiks, the masons began to pull down their work, and whin they went an for some time, the bishop bid them stop, and he'd let them down; but faiks, before he gev in to them they had taken the roof clane off; and that's the raison that one tower has a roof, sir, and the other has none."

But before I had seen Clonmacnoise and its towers, I was intimate with the most striking of its legends, by favour of the sinewy boatman who rowed me to it. We had not long left Shannonbridge when, doubling an angle of the shore and stretching up a reach of the river where it widens, the principal round tower of Clonmacnoise became visible.

"What tower is that?" said I to my Charon.

"That's the big tower of Clonmacnoise, sir," he answered. "An', if your honour looks sharp a little to the right of it, lower down, you'll see the ruins of the ould palace."

On a somewhat closer inspection, I did perceive the remains he spoke of, dimly discernible in the distance; and it was not without his indication of their relative situation to the tower that I could have distinguished them from the sober grey of the horizon behind them, for the evening was closing fast, and we were moving eastward.

"Does your honour see it yit?" said my boatman.

"I do," said I.

"God spare you your eyesight," responded he, "for troth it's few gintleman could see the ould palace this far off, and the sun so low, barrin' they were used to spottin', and had a sharp eye for the birds over a bog, or the like o' that. Oh, then it's Clonmacnoise, your honour, that's the holy place," continued he. "Mighty holy in the ould ancient times, and mighty great too, wid the sivin churches, let alone the two towers, and the bishop, and plinty o' priests, and all to that."

"Two towers?" said I. "Then I suppose one has fallen?"

"Not at all, sir," said he, "but the other one that you can't see, is beyant in the hollow by the river side."

"And it was a great place, you say, in the ould ancient times?"

"Troth it was, sir, and is still, for to this day it bates the world in regard o' pilgrims."

"Pilgrims!" I ejaculated.

"Yes, sir," said the boatman, with his own quiet manner; although it was evident to a quick observer that my surprise at the mention of pilgrims had not escaped him.

I mused a moment. Pilgrims, thought I, in the British dominions, in the nineteenth century—strange enough!

"And so," continued I aloud, "you have pilgrims at Clonmacnoise?"

"Troth we have, your honour, from the top of the north and the farthest corner of Kerry. And may you see them any day in the week, let alone the pathern [patron] day, when all the world, you'd think, was there."

"And the palace," said I, "I suppose belonged to the bishop of Clonmacnoise?"

"Some says 'twas the bishop, your honour, and indeed it is them that has larnin' says so. But more says 'twas a King had it long ago, afore the churches was there at all, at all. And sure enough it looks far oulder nor the churches though them is ould enough in all conscience. All the knowledge people I ever heerd talk of it, says that. And now, sir," said he in an expostulatory tone, "wouldn't it be far more nath'ral that the bishop id live in the churches? And sure," continued he, evidently leaning to the popular belief, "it stands to raison that a King id live in a palace, and why shud it be called a palace if a King didn't live there?"

Satisfying himself with this most logical conclusion, he pulled his oar with evident self-complacency. As I have always found, I derived more legendary information by yielding somewhat to the narrator, and by abstaining from inflicting any wound on his pride by endeavouring to combat his credulity. I seemed to favour his conclusions, and admitted that a King must have been the former occupant of the palace.

So much being settled, he proceeded to tell me that "there was a mighty quare story" about the last King that ruled Clonmacnoise and, pulling his oar with an easier sweep lest he might disturb the quiet hearing of his legend, he prepared to tell his tale.

"Well, sir, they say there was a King wanst lived in the palace beyant and a sportin' fellow he was, and 'Cead mile failte' was the word in the palace; no one kem but was welkem, and I go bail the sorra one left it without the 'deoch an' doris'. Well, to be sure, the King av coorse had the best of eatin' and drinkin', and there was bed and boord for the stranger, let alone the welkim for the neighbour—and a good neighbour he was, by all accounts. Until, as bad luck would have it, a crass ould bishop (the saints forgi' me for saying the word) kem to rule over the churches. Now, you must know, the King was a likely man and, as I said already, he was a sportin' fellow, and by coorse a great favourite with the women; he had a smile and a wink for the crathers at every hand's turn, and the soft word, and the—the short and the long of it is, he was the divil among the girls.

"Well, sir, it was all mighty well, untell the ould bishop I mentioned arrived at the churches; but whin he kem, he tuck great scandal at the goings-an of the King, and he determined to cut him short in his coorses all at wanst. So with that whin the King wint to his duty, the bishop ups and he tells him that he must mend his manners, and all to that; and when the King said that the likes o' that was never told him afore by the best priest o' them all, 'More shame for them that wor before me,' says the bishop.

"But to make a long story short, the King looked mighty black at the bishop, and the bishop looked twice blacker at him again, and so on, from bad to worse, till they parted the bittherest of inimies. And the King that was the best o' friends to the churches afore, swore be this and be that, he'd vex them for it, and that he'd be even with the bishop afore long.

"Now, sir, the bishop might jist as well have kept never minding the King's little kimneens with the girls, for the story goes that he had a little failin' of his own in regard of a dhrop, and that he knew the differ betune wine and wather, for, poor ignorant crathurs, it's little they knew about whiskey in them days.

"Well, the King used often to send lashins o' wine to the

churches, by the way, as he said, that they should have plinty of it for celebrating the Mass. He knew well that it was a little of it went far that-a-way, and that their Riverinces was fond of a hearty glass as well as himself. And why not, sir, if they'd let him alone?

" 'For,' says the King, as many a one said afore, and will again, 'I'll make a child's bargain with you,' says he. 'Do you let me alone, and I'll let you alone.' Manin' by that, sir, that if they'd say nothin' about the girls, he would give them plenty of wine.

"So it fell out a little before he had the scrimmage with the bishop, the King promised them a fine store of wine that was comin' up the Shannon in boats, sir. And big boats they wor, I'll go bail, not all as one as the little drolleen [wren] of a thing we're in now, but high-hand as big as a ship. And there was three of these fine boats full comin'—two for himself, and one for the churches.

"So says the King to himself, 'The divil receave the dhrop of that wine they shall get,' says he, 'the dirty beggarly neygars. Bad cess to the dhrop,' says he, 'my big-bellied bishop, to nourish your jolly red nose. I said I'd be even with you,' says he, 'and so I will. And if you spoil my divarshin, I'll spoil yours, and turn about is fair play, as the divil said to the smoke-jack.'

"With that, sir, the King goes and he gives ordhers to his sarvants how it wid be when the boats kem up the river with the wine—and more especial to one in partic'lar they called Corny, his own man, by raison he was mighty stout, and didn't love priest much more nor himself.

"Now Corny, sir, let alone bein' stout, was mighty dark, and if he wanst said the word, you might as well sthrive to move the rock of Dunamaise as Corny, though without a big word at all, at all, but as quite [quiet] as a child.

"Well, in good time, up kem the boats, and down runs the monks, all as one as a flock o' crows over a corn-field, to pick up whatever they could for themselves; but troth the King was afore them, for all his men was there with Corny at their head.

" 'Dominus vobiscum'—which manes, 'God save you,' sir—says one of the monks to Corny. 'We kem down to save you the throuble of unloadin' the wine, which the King, God bless him, gives to the church.'

" 'Oh, no trouble in life, plaze your Riverince,' says Corny, 'we'll unload it ourselves, your Riverince,' says he.

"With that they began unloadin', first one boat, and then another; but sure enough, every individual cashk of it went up to the palace, and not a one to the churches. So whin they seen the second boat a'most empty, quare thoughts began to come into their heads, for before this offer, the first boatload was always sent to the bishop, afore a dhrop was taken to the King, which, you know, was good manners, sir—and the king, by all accounts, was a gintleman, every inch of him.

"With that, says one of the monks: 'My blessin' an you, Corny, my son,' says he. 'Sure it's not forgettin' the bishop you'd be, nor the churches,' says he, 'that stands betune you and the Divil?'

"Well, sir, at the word Divil, 'twas as good as a play to see the look Corny gave out o' the corner of his eye at the monk.

" 'Forget yez?' says Corny. 'Troth it's long afore me or my masther,' says he—nodding his head a bit at the word—'will forget the bishop of Clonmacnoise. Go an with your work, boys,' says he to the men about him, and away they wint, and soon finished unloadin' the second boat. And with that they began at the third.

" 'God bless your work, boys,' says the bishop—for, sure enough, 'twas the bishop himself kem down to the river side, having got the hard word of what was goin' an. 'God bless your work,' says he, as they heaved the first barrel of wine out of the boat. 'Go, help them, my sons,' says he, turnin' round to half a dozen strappin' young priests as was standing by.

" 'No occasion in life, plaze your Riverince,' says Corny. 'I'm intirely obleeged to your lordship, but we're able for the work ourselves,' says he. And without sayin' another word, away went the barrel out of the boat, and up on their shoulders, or whatever way they wor takin' it, and up the hill to the palace.

" 'Hillo!' says the bishop. 'Where are yiz goin' with that wine?' says he.

" 'Where I tould them,' says Corny.

" 'Is it to the palace?' says his Riverince.

" 'Faith, you jist hit it,' says Corny.

" 'And what's that for?' says the bishop.

" 'For fun,' says Corny, no way frikened at all by the dark look the bishop gave him. And sure it's a wondher the fear of the Church didn't keep him in dread—but Corny was the divil intirely.

" 'Is that the answer you give your clergy, you reprobate?' says the bishop. 'I'll tell you what it is, Corny,' says he. 'As sure as you're standin' there I'll excommunicate you, my fine fellow, if you don't keep a civil tongue in your head.'

" 'Sure it wouldn't be worth your Riverince's while,' says Corny, 'to excommunicate the likes o' me,' says he, 'while there's the King my masther to the fore, for your Holiness to play bell, book, and candle-light with.'

" 'Do you mane to say, you scruff o' the earth,' says the bishop, 'that your masther, the King, put you up to what you're doing?'

" 'Divil a thing else I mane,' says Corny.

" 'You villain!' says the bishop. 'The King never did the like.'

" 'Yes, but I did though,' says the King, puttin' in his word fair and aisy, for he was lookin' out o' his dhrawin'-room windy, and had run down the hill to the river, when he seen the bishop goin', as he thought, to put his comether upon Corny.

" 'So,' says the bishop, turnin' round quite short to the King, 'so, my lord,' says he, 'am I to understand this villian has your commands for his purty behaviour?'

" 'He has my commands for what he has done,' says the King, quite stout. 'And more to be token, I'd have you to know he's no villain at all,' says he, 'but a thrusty sarvant, who does his masther's biddin'.'

" 'And don't you intind sendin' any of this wine over to my churches beyant?' says the bishop.

" 'Bad luck to the dhrop,' says the King.

" 'And what for?' says the bishop.

" 'Bekase I've changed my mind,' says the King.

" 'And won't you give the Church wine for the holy Mass?' says the bishop.

" 'The Mass!' says the King, eyein' him mighty sly.

" 'Yes, sir—the Mass,' says his Riverince, colouring up to the eyes, 'the Mass.'

" 'Oh, baithershin,' says the King.

" 'What do you mane?' says the bishop—and his nose got blue with rage.

" 'Oh, nothin',' says the King, with a toss of his head.

" 'Are you a gintleman?' says the bishop.

" 'Every inch o' me,' says the King.

" 'Then sure no gintleman goes back of his word,' says the other.

"I won't go back o' my word, either,' says the King. 'I promised to give wine for the Mass,' says he, 'and so I will. Send to my palace every Sunday mornin', and you shall have a bottle of wine, and that's plinty. For I'm thinkin',' says the King, 'that so much wine lyin' beyant there, is neither good for your bodies nor your sowls.'

" 'What do you mane?' says the bishop in a great passion, for all the world like a turkey-cock.

" 'I mane, that when your wine-cellar is so full,' says the King, 'it only brings the fairies about you, and makes away with the wine too fast,' says he laughin'. 'And for the fairies to be about the churches isn't good, your Riverince,' says the King. 'For I'm thinkin',' says he, 'that some of the spiteful little divils has given your Riverince a blast, and burnt the ind of your nose.'

"With that, my dear, you couldn't hould the bishop, with the rage he was in, and says he, 'You think to dhrink all that wine—but you're mistaken,' says he. 'Fill your cellars as much as you like,' says the bishop, 'but you'll die in drooth yit.'

"With that he went down on his knees and cursed the King—God betune us and harm!—and shakin' his fist at him, he gother [gathered] all his monks about him, and away they wint home to the churches.

"Well, sir, sure enough, the King fell sick of a sudden, and all the docthors in the country round was sent for, but they could do him no good at all, at all. Day by day he was wastin' and wastin', and pinin' and pinin', till the flesh was worn off his bones, and he was as bare and yellow as a kite's claw. Then, what would you think, but the drooth came an him sure enough, and he was callin' for dhrink every minit, till you'd think he'd dhrink the sae dhry.

"Well, when the clock struck twelve that night, the drooth was an him worse nor ever, though he dhrunk as much that day—ay, troth, as much as would turn a mill; and he called to his servants for a drink of grule [gruel].

" 'The grule's all out,' says they.

" 'Well, then give me some whay,' says he.

" 'There's none left, my lord,' says they.

" 'Then give me a dhrink of wine,' says he.

" 'There's none in the room, dear,' says the nurse-tindher.

" 'Then go down to the wine-cellar,' says he, 'and get some.'

"With that, they wint to the wine-cellar—but, jew'l machree, they soon run back into his room, with their faces as white as a sheet, and tould him there was not one dhrop of wine in all the cashks in the cellar.

" 'Oh murther! murther!' says the King, 'I'm dyin' of drooth,' say he.

"And then—God help iz!—they bethought themselves of what the bishop said, and the curse he laid an the King.

" 'You've no grule?' says the King.

" 'No,' says they.

" 'Nor whay?'

" 'No,' says the sarvants.

" 'Nor wine?' says the King.

" 'Nor wine either, my Lord,' says they.

" 'Have you no tay?' says he.

" 'Not a dhrop,' says the nurse-tindher.

" 'Then,' says the King, 'for the tindher marcy of heaven, gi' me a dhrink of wather.'

"And what would you think, sir, but there wasn't a dhrop of wather in the palace.

" 'Oh, murther, murther!' says the King. 'Isn't it a poor case, that a King can't get a dhrink of wather in his own house? Go then,' says he, 'and get me a jug of wather out of the ditch.'

"For there was a big ditch, sir, round the palace. And away they run for wather out of the ditch, while the King was roarin' like mad for the drooth, and his mouth like a coal of fire. And sure, sir, as the story goes, they coundn't find any wather in the ditch!

" 'Millia murther! Millia murther!' cries the King. 'Will no one take pity an a King that's dyin' for the bare drooth?'

"And they thrimbled again, with the fair fright, when they heerd this, and thought of the ould bishop's prophecy.

" 'Well,' says the poor King, 'run down to the Shannon,' says he, 'and sure, at all events, you'll get wather there,' says he.

"Well, sir, away they run with pails and noggins down to the Shannon, and—God betune us and harm!—what do you think, sir, but the river Shannon was dhry! So, av coors, when the King heerd the Shannon was gone dhry, it wint to his heart; and he thought o' the bishop's curse an him—and, givin' one mutherin' big screech, that split the walls of the palace, as may be seen to this day, he died, sir—makin' the bishop's words good, that 'he would die of drooth yet'.

"And now, sir," says my historian, with a look of lurking humour in his dark grey eye, "isn't that mighty wondherful? In it's thrue."

Fin MacCumhail and the Son of the King of Alba

BY JEREMIAH CURTIN

n a day Fin went out hunting with his dog Bran, on Knock an Ar, and he killed so much game that he didn't know what to do with it or how to bring it home. As he stood looking and thinking, all at once he saw a man running towards him, with a rope around his waist so long that half his body was covered with it; and the man was of such size that, as he ran, Fin could see the whole world between his legs and nothing between his head and the sky. When he came up, the man saluted Fin, who answered him most kindly. "Where are you going?" asked Fin.

"I am out looking for a master."

"Well," said Fin, "I am in sore need of a man. What can you do?"

"Do you see this rope on my body? Whatever this rope will bind, I can carry."

"If that is true," said Fin, "you are the man I want. Do you see the game on this hillside?"

"I do," said the man.

"Well, put that into the rope and carry it to my castle."

The man put all the game into the rope, made a great bundle, and threw it on his back.

"Show me the way to the castle now," said he.

Fin started on ahead, and though he ran with all his might, he could not gain one step on the man who followed with the game. The sentry on guard at the castle saw the man running while yet far off. He stepped inside the gate and said: "There is a man coming with a load on his back as big as a mountain." Before he could come out again to his place the man was there and the load

69

off his back. When the game came to the ground, it shook the castle to its foundations.

Next day the man was sent to herd cows for a time, and while he was gone, Conan Maol said to Fin: "If you don't put this cowherd to death, he will destroy all the Fenians of Erin."

"How could I put such a good man to death?" asked Fin.

"Send him," said Conan, "to sow corn on the brink of a lake in the north of Erin. Now, in that lake lives a serpent that never lets a person pass, but swallows every man that goes that way."

Fin agreed to this, and the next morning after breakfast he called the man, gave him seven bullocks, a plough, and a sack of grain, and sent him to the lake in the north of Erin to sow corn.

When the man came to the lake, he started to plough, drew one furrow. The lake began to boil up, and as he was coming back, making the second furrow, the serpent was on the field before him and swallowed the seven bullocks and the plough up to the handles. But the man held fast to what he had in his two hands, gave a pull, and dragged the plough and six of the bullocks out of the belly of the serpent. The seventh one remained inside. The serpent went at him and they fought for seven days and nights. At the end of that time the serpent was as tame as a cat, and the man drove him and the six bullocks home before him.

When he was in sight of Fin's castle, the sentry at the gate ran in and cried: "That cowherd is coming with the size of a mountain before him!"

"Run out," said Conan Maol, "and tell him to tie the serpent to that oak out there."

They ran out, and the man tied the serpent to the oak tree, then came in and had a good supper.

Next morning the man went out to herd cows as before. "Well," said Conan Maol to Fin, "if you don't put this man to death, he'll destroy you and me and all the Fenians of Erin."

"How could I put such a man to death?"

"There is," said Conan, "a bullock in the north of Erin, and he drives fog out of himself for seven days and then he draws it in for seven other days. Tomorrow is the last day for drawing it in. If any one man comes near, he'll swallow him alive."

When the cowherd came to supper in the evening, Fin said to him: "I am going to have a feast and need fresh beef. Now there is a bullock in that same valley by the lake in the north of Erin where you punished the serpent and if you go there and bring the bullock to me, you'll have my thanks."

"I'll go," said the man, "the first thing after breakfast in the morning."

So off he went next morning, and when he came near the valley, he found the bullock asleep and drawing in the last of the fog. Soon he found himself going in with it. So he caught hold of a great oak-tree for safety. The bullock woke up then and saw him, and letting a roar out of himself, faced him, and gave him a pitch with his horn which sent him seven miles over the top of a wood. And when he fell to the ground, the bullock was on him again before he had time to rise, and gave him another pitch which sent him back and broke three ribs in his body.

"This will never do," said the man, as he rose and, pulling up an oak tree by the roots for a club, he faced the bullock. And there they were at one another for five days and nights, till the bullock was as tame as a cat and the man drove him home to Fin's castle.

The sentry saw them coming and ran inside the gate with word.

"Tell the man to tie the bullock to that oak tree beyond," said Conan. "We don't want him near this place."

The cowherd tied the bullock, and told Fin to send four of the best butchers in Erin to kill him with an axe; and the four of them struck him one after another and any of them couldn't knock him.

"Give me an axe," said the man to the butchers. They gave him the axe, and the first stroke he gave, he knocked the bullock. Then they began to skin him, but the man didn't like the way they were doing the work, so he took his sword and had three quarters of the bullock skinned before they could skin one.

Next morning the cowherd went out with the cows, but he wasn't long gone when Conan Maol came to Fin and said: "If you don't put an end to that man, he'll soon put an end to you and to me and to all of us, so there won't be a man of the Fenians of Erin left alive."

"How could I put an end to a man like him?" asked Fin.

"There is in the north of Erin," said Conan, "a wild sow who has two great pigs of her own. She and her two pigs have bags of poison in their tails, and when they see any man, they run at him and shake their poison bags; and if the smallest drop of the poison touches him, it is death to him that minute. If by any chance he should escape the wild sow and the pigs, there is a fox-man called the Gruagach, who has but one eye and that in the middle of his forehead. The Gruagach carries a club of a ton weight, and if the cowherd gets one welt of that club, he'll never trouble the Fenians of Erin again."

Next morning Fin called up the cowherd and said: "I am going to have a feast in this castle, and I would like to have some fresh pork. There is a wild sow in the north of Erin with two pigs, and if you bring her to me before the feast, you'll have my thanks."

"I'll go and bring her to you," said the cowherd.

So after breakfast he took his sword, went to the north of Erin, and stole up to the sow and two pigs, and whipped the tails off the three of them, before they knew he was in it. Then he faced the wild sow and fought with her for four days and five nights, and on the morning of the fifth day he knocked her dead. At the last blow, his sword stuck in her backbone and he couldn't draw it out. But with one pull he broke the blade, and stood there over her with only the hilt in his hand. Then he put his foot on one of her jaws, took the other in his hands and, splitting her evenly from the nose to the tail, made two halves of her.

He threw one half on his shoulder; and that minute the big Gruagach with one eye in his head came along and made an offer of his club at him to kill him. But the cowherd jumped aside, and catching the Gruagach by one of his legs, threw him up on to the half of the wild sow on his shoulder, and taking the other half of her from the ground, clapped that on the top of the Gruagach, and ran away to Fin's castle as fast as his legs could carry him.

The sentry at the castle gate ran in and said: "The cowherd is running to the castle, and the size of a mountain on his back."

"Go out now," said Conan Maol, "and stop him where he is, or he'll throw down the castle if he comes here with the load that's on him."

But before the sentry was back at his place, the cowherd was at the gate shaking the load off his back and the castle to its foundations, so that every dish and vessel in it was broken to bits.

The Gruagach jumped from the ground, rubbed his legs and every part of him that was sore from the treatment he got. He was so much in dread of the cowherd that he ran with all the strength that was in him, and never stopped to look back till he was in the north of Erin.

Next morning the cowherd went out with the cows, drove them back in the evening; and while picking the thigh-bone of a bullock for his supper, Oscar, son of Oisin, the strongest man of the Fenians of Erin, came up to him and took hold of the bone to pull it from his hand. The cowherd held one end and Oscar the other, and pulled till they made two halves of the bone.

"What did you carry away?" asked the cowherd.

"What I have in my hand," said Oscar.

"And I kept what I held in my fist," said the cowherd.

"There is that for you now," said Oscar, and he hit him a slap.

The cowherd said no word in answer, but next morning he asked his wages of Fin.

"Oh, then," said Fin, "I'll pay you and welcome, for you are the best man I have ever had or met with."

Then the cowherd went away to Cahirciveen in Kerry where he had an enchanted castle. But before he went he invited Fin MacCumhail and the Fenians of Erin to have a great feast with him. "For," said he to Fin, "I'm not a cowherd at all, but the son of the King of Alba, and I'll give you good cheer."

When the Fenians came to the place, they found the finest castle that could be seen. There were three fires in each room and seven spits at every fire. When they had gone and sat down in their places, there was but one fire in each room.

"Rise up, every man of you," said Fin, "or we are lost; for this is an enchanted place."

They tried to rise, but each man was fastened to his seat, and the seat to the floor; and not one of them could stir. Then the last fire went out and they were in darkness.

"Chew your thumb," said Conan to Fin, "and try is there any way out of here."

Fin chewed his thumb and knew what trouble they were in. Then he put his two hands into his mouth and blew the old-time whistle. And this whistle was heard by Pogan and Ceolan, two sons of Fin who were in the North at that time, one fishing and the other hurling.

When they heard the whistle, they said: "Our father and the Fenians of Erin are in trouble." And they faced towards the sound and never stopped till they knocked at the door of the enchanted castle of the son of Alba at Cahirciveen.

"Who is there?" asked Fin.

"Your two sons," said one of them.

"Well," said Fin, "we are in danger of death tonight. That cowherd I had in my service was no cowherd at all, but the son of the King of Alba, and his father has said that he will not eat three meals off one table without having my head. There is an army now on the road to kill us tonight. There is no way in or out of this castle but by one ford, and to that ford the army of the King of Alba is coming."

The two sons of Fin went out at nightfall and stood in the ford before the army. The son of the King of Alba knew them well, and calling each by name, said: "Won't you let us pass?"

"We will not," said they; and then the fight began. The two sons of Fin MacCumhail, Pogan and Ceolan, destroyed the whole army and killed every man except the son of the King of Alba.

After the battle the two went back to their father. "We have destroyed the whole army at the ford," said they.

"There is a greater danger ahead," said Fin. "There is an old hag coming with a little pot. She will dip her finger in the pot, touch the lips of the dead men, and bring the whole army to life. But first of all there will be music at the ford, and if you hear the music, you'll fall asleep. Now go, but if you do not overpower the old hag, we are lost."

"We'll do the best we can," said the two sons of Fin.

They were not long at the ford when one said: "I am falling asleep from that music."

"So am I," said the other.

"Knock your foot down on mine," said the first.

The other kicked his foot and struck him, but no use. Then each took his spear and drove it through the foot of the other, but both fell asleep in spite of the spears.

The old hag went on touching the lips of the dead men, who stood up alive, and she was crossing the ford at the head of the army when she stumbled over the two sleeping brothers and spilt what was in the pot over their bodies.

They sprang up fresh and well, and picking up two stones of a ton weight each that were there in the ford, they made for the champions of Alba and never stopped till they killed the last man of them. Then they killed the old hag herself.

Pogan and Ceolan then knocked at the door of the castle.

"Who's there?" asked Fin.

"Your two sons," said they. "And we have killed all the champions of Alba and the old hag as well."

"You have more to do yet," said Fin. "There are three kings in the north of Erin who have three silver goblets. These kings are holding a feast in a fort today. You must go and cut the heads off the three, put their blood in the goblets and bring them here. When you come, rub the blood on the keyhole of the door and it will open before you. When you come in, rub the seats and we shall all be free."

The three goblets of blood were brought to Cahirciveen, the door of the castle flew open, and light came into every room. The brothers rubbed blood on the chairs of all the Fenians of Erin and freed them all, except Conan Maol, who had no chair, but sat on the floor with his back to the wall. When they came to him the last drop of blood was gone.

All the Fenians of Erin were hurrying past, anxious to escape, and paid no heed to Conan, who had never a good word in his mouth for any man. Then Conan turned to Diarmuid, and said: "If a woman were here in place of me, you wouldn't leave her to die this way."

Then Diarmuid turned, took him by one hand, and Goll MacMorna by the other and, pulling with all their might, tore him from the wall and the floor. But as they did, he left all the skin of his back from his head to his heels on the floor and the wall behind him. But when they were going home through the hills of Tralee, they found a sheep on the way, killed it, and clapped the skin on Conan. The sheepskin grew to his body and he was so well and strong that they sheared him every year, and got wool enough from his back to make flannel and frieze for the Fenians of Erin ever after.

The Fianna

TRANSLATED BY
STANDISH HAYES O'GRADY

his is the enumeration of Finn's people. Their strength was seven-score-and-ten officers, each man of these having thrice nine warriors, every one bound (as was the way with Cuchulainn in the time when he was there) to certain conditions of service. Namely that in satisfaction of a guarantee violated they must not accept material compensation in the matter of valuables or of meat; must not deny any guarantee; nor any single individual of them fly before warriors.

Not a man was taken into the Fianna nor admitted whether to the great Gathering of Usnach, to the Convention of Taillte, or to Tara's Feast, until both his paternal and his maternal co-relatives, his tuatha and kindreds, had given securities for him to the effect that though at the present instant he were slain, yet should not claim be urged in lieu of him. This in order that to none other but to themselves alone should the Fianna look to avenge themselves. On the other hand, in the case it were they inflicted great mischiefs upon others, reprisals were not to be made upon their relatives.

Again not a man was taken until he was a prime poet versed in the twelve books of poetic composition. No man was taken till in the ground a large hole had been made (such as to reach the fold of his belt) and he put into it with his shield and a forearm's length of a hazel stick. Then must nine warriors, having nine spears, with a ten furrows' width betwixt them and him, assail him and in concert let fly at him. If past that guard of his he were hurt then, he was not received into Fianship.

Not a man of them was taken till his hair had been interwoven into braids on him and he started at a run through Ireland's woods; while they, seeking to wound him, followed in his wake, there having been between him and them but one forest bough

by way of interval at first. Should he be overtaken, he was wounded and not received into the Fianna after. If his weapons had quivered in his hand, he was not taken. Should a branch in the wood have disturbed anything of his hair out of its braiding, neither was he taken. If he had cracked a dry stick under his foot as he ran, he was not accepted. Unless that at full speed he had both jumped a stick level with his brow and stooped to pass under one even with his knee, he was not taken. Also, unless without slackening his pace he could with his nail extract a thorn from his foot, he was not taken into Fianship. But if he performed all this he was of Finn's people.

15th or 16th CENTURY

Diarmuid and Grainne

ADAPTED BY MARY McGARRY

On the death of his wife, Manissa, the daughter of Garad of the Black Knee, Finn MacCumhail sought the hand of the young and beautiful daughter of King Cormac MacArt called Grainne. The King approved of the match and feasted Finn and his Fianna men at Tara. However, during the celebrations it chanced that Grainne sat next to Diarmuid, one of Finn's bravest warriors, renowned for his courage and high-mindedness.

Now, since the fair Grainne felt nothing for Finn, who was indeed even older than her own father, she appealed to Diarmuid to save her from a hateful marriage, having at first sight fallen deeply in love with the young hero.

Diarmuid was greatly disturbed for he could not help loving the princess with all his heart, but he wished to hide this as he put his duty to his chief above all else. However, seeing this, Grainne placed Diarmuid under a "geasa" and under bonds of heavy druidical spells—bonds that true heroes never break through—to take her away before Finn and the rest awoke for the wedding.

Diarmuid sought advice from his friends; of these even Oisin, the son of Finn, said that under such a bond he should leave Tara with the princess, but forever beware of the wrath of Finn.

So Diarmuid and Grainne plighted their faith and vowed solemnly to be true to each other as man and wife for ever.

The couple fled from Tara, first by chariot as far as the ford of Athlone, where Diarmuid carried Grainne across the water and they continued on foot. When they reached the Wood of the Two Tents, Diarmuid built a hut of branches where the couple rested.

Meanwhile Finn, burning with jealousy and rage, ordered the

tracking-men, the Clann Navin, to pursue them. When all tracks disappeared at Athlone, Finn in a fit of anger told the trackers that unless they took up the track again speedily, he would hang every man of the Clann Navin on the edge of the ford.

When the pursuers came to the Wood of the Two Tents, it seemed certain that Diarmuid and his love would be discovered. But Oisin and others who cared for Diarmuid sent Finn's hound, Bran, to warn him of the approach of the Fianna.

However, despite Grainne's fears, Diarmuid refused to flee till Finn had overtaken them. For the hero had cleared a space round the hut and surrounded it with a fence that no man could pierce, with seven narrow doors of strong poles woven with saplings, to face seven different parts of the wood. Finn stationed his men around the fence to wait for the couple to attempt to escape.

Now Angus of Brugh, the wisest and the most skilled in magic arts of all the Dedannan race, was Diarmuid's foster-father. He had taught him all the arts and accomplishments of a champion and loved him as a father does his only son. It was revealed to Angus that Diarmuid was in great danger, so he arose and travelled on the wings of the east wind to the Wood of the Two Tents, and entered the hut without being perceived by Finn and his men. Diarmuid warmly greeted the old man, and on hearing their story Angus summoned the pair to escape under his mantle, without Finn's knowledge. But Diarmuid was determined to stay and face Finn. If he should be slain he asked that Grainne be restored to her father. Angus then took Grainne safely away as far as the Wood of the Two Sallows, now called Limerick.

Diarmuid girded on his armour, and marched, weapon in hand, to one of the seven narrow doors and asked who was outside. Oisin and Oscar replied that it was they who guarded this door and that he had nothing to fear from them. But Diarmuid wished to find the door which Finn himself guarded. At the second and third doors more friends promised to help him, but Diarmuid repeated that he would not go out as it would only bring Finn's displeasure on those that acted kindly to him. At one door the Clann Navin threatened him with their spears, but he went on until he reached the door behind which Finn himself stood. At that door, Diarmuid found an unguarded place, rose by means of his two spears with a light, airy bound over the fence and landed on the clear space outside. Running swiftly, he was soon out of reach of sword and spear. Happily he sped towards the Wood of the Two Sallows and rejoined his princess.

However Angus realised that Finn would still seek the couple and counselled them well as to what they should do before he left them. Indeed Diarmuid and Grainne had many more adventures and perils to face in their flight from the revenge of Finn; local people still point out their resting places of refuge, called the "Beds of Diarmuid and Grainne".

Finally Angus went to Finn and asked him to make peace with Diarmuid. Finn, seeing he could not overcome the hero, told Angus he was weary of the quarrel and ready to agree to peace on whatever terms Diarmuid chose. King Cormac was also ready to forgive his son-in-law and give his other daughter to Finn as a wife.

Diarmuid and Grainne settled far away from both Finn and Cormac on land granted to them, and their family grew in number and prosperity as the years went by. But one day Grainne, sad to be so far removed from the world, asked Diarmuid that her father and Finn might visit their house. Unluckily Diarmuid consented and a great feast was held for the guests.

One night, Diarmuid heard the call of a hound and wished to investigate the sound that thus disturbed the night. Grainne in fear cautioned him, but the next day Diarmuid would be held back no longer, regardless of any danger that Grainne's heart foretold. Diarmuid set out and came to the summit of Ben-Gulben, where he found Finn. The Fianna were chasing the wild boar of Ben-Gulben which, having already slain many of his pursuers, was heading towards the very hillock where the two men stood.

Diarmuid was not likely to flee before a mere boar, but Finn told Diarmuid that, although he did not know it, he was under a "geasa" never to hunt a boar. The old warrior explained that a youth slain several years before by Donn, Diarmuid's father, was changed at the moment of his death into a druidic boar, and appointed to slay the son of his murderer. Angus had known this and commanded that the child should never hunt a wild boar.

Having said this, Finn parted from Diarmuid, who attacked the boar with his usual courage. But neither spear nor arm could harm the boar, and as he finally stood defenceless the animal gashed the warrior's side with his tusk, making a deep wound. Diarmuid prevented another attack by flinging his sword through the skull of the boar, who fell dead.

Finn and the Fianna arrived to find the hero bleeding to death. Diarmuid appealed to Finn to use his gift of healing to save him, by giving him a drink of water from the closed palms of his two

hands. Finn hesitated and Diarmuid recalled the times when he had helped his leader, but Finn could not forget Grainne and Diarmuid's betrayal at Tara.

Yet when all around him were moved to pity for the dying man, Finn at last went to a nearby well in search of water. But after he had walked a short way he let it spill through his fingers. Again he went to the well, but at the thought of Grainne the water spilt out yet once more. Finn was hastening forward for a third time when Diarmuid's head dropped back as he left this life.

Grainne and the Fianna wept for the man they loved so much, and Angus in deep grief that he had not been there to prevent the doom of his favourite son, carried the body of the dead hero to its last resting place near him at Brugh.

Oisin in Tir Na nOg
or The Last of the Fena

BY P. W. JOYCE

*According to an ancient legend, Finn's son, Oisin, the hero-poet,
survived to the time of St. Patrick, two hundred years (the
legend makes it three hundred) after the other Fena. On a certain
occasion, when the saint asked him how he had lived to such a
great age, the old hero related the following story.*

a short time after the fatal battle of Gavra, where so
many of our heroes fell, we were hunting on a dewy
morning near the brink of Loch Lein, where the
trees and hedges around us were all fragrant with blossoms, and
the little birds sang melodious music on the branches. We soon
roused the deer from the thickets, and as they bounded over the
plain, our hounds in full cry followed after them.

We were not long so engaged, when we saw a rider coming
swiftly towards us from the west; and we soon perceived that
it was a maiden on a white steed. We all ceased from the chase
on seeing the lady, who reined in as she approached. And Finn
and the Fena were greatly surprised, for they had never before
seen so lovely a maiden. A slender golden diadem encircled her
head. She wore a brown robe of silk, spangled with stars of red
gold, which was fastened in front by a golden brooch, and fell
from her shoulders till it swept the ground. Her yellow hair
flowed far down over her robe in bright, golden ringlets. Her blue
eyes were as clear as the drops of dew on the grass and while her
small, white hand held the bridle and curbed her steed with a
golden bit, she sat more gracefully than a swan on Loch Lein.

The white steed was covered with a smooth, flowing mantle.
He was shod with four shoes of pure yellow gold, and in all Erin
a better or more beautiful steed could not be found.

As she came slowly to the presence of Finn, he addressed her courteously: "Who art thou, O lovely youthful princess? Tell us thy name and the name of thy country, and relate to us the cause of thy coming."

She answered in a sweet and gentle voice: "Noble King of the Fena, I have had a long journey this day, for my country lies far off in the Western Sea. I am the daughter of the King of Tir na nOg, and my name is Niamh of the Golden Hair."

"And what is it that has caused thee to come so far across the sea? Has thy husband forsaken thee? Or what other evil has befallen thee?"

"My husband has not forsaken me, for I have never been married or betrothed to any man. But I love thy noble son, Oisin, and this is what has brought me to Erin. It is not without reason that I have given him my love, and that I have undertaken this long journey. For I have often heard of his bravery, his gentleness, and the nobleness of his person. Many princes and high chiefs have sought me in marriage, but I was quite indifferent to all men and never consented to wed, till my heart was moved with love for thy gentle son, Oisin."

When I heard these words, and when I looked on the lovely maiden with her glossy, golden hair, I was all over in love with her. I came near, and, taking her small hand in mine, I told her she was a mild star of brightness and beauty, and that I preferred her to all the princesses in the world for my wife.

"Then," said she, "I place you under 'geasa', which true heroes never break through, to come with me on my white steed to Tir na nOg, the land of never-ending youth. It is the most delightful and the most renowned country under the sun. There is abundance of gold and silver and jewels, of honey and wine; and the trees bear fruit and blossoms and green leaves together all the year round.

"You will get a hundred swords and a hundred robes of silk and satin, a hundred swift steeds, and a hundred slender, keen-scenting hounds. You will get herds of cows without number, flocks of sheep with fleeces of gold, a coat of mail that cannot be pierced, and a sword that never missed a stroke and from which no one ever escaped alive.

"There are feasting and harmless pastimes each day. A hundred warriors fully armed shall always await you at call, and harpers shall delight you with their sweet music. You will wear the diadem of the King of Tir na nOg, which he never yet gave to

88

anyone under the sun, and which will guard you day and night, in tumult and battle and danger of every kind.

"Lapse of time shall bring neither decay nor death, and you shall be for ever young, and gifted with unfading beauty and strength. All these delights you shall enjoy, and many others that I do not mention; and I myself will be your wife if you come with me to Tir na nOg."

I replied that she was my choice above all the maidens in the world, and that I would willingly go with her to the Land of Youth.

When my father, Finn, and the Fena heard me say this, and knew that I was going from them, they raised three shouts of grief and lamentation. And Finn came up to me and took my hand in his, saying sadly: "Woe is me, my son, that you are going away from me, for I do not expect that you will ever return to me."

The manly beauty of his countenance became quite dimmed with sorrow, and though I promised to return after a little time, and fully believed that I should see him again, I could not check my tears as I gently kissed my father's cheek.

I then bade farewell to my dear companions, and mounted the white steed, while the lady kept her seat before me. She gave the signal, and the steed galloped swiftly and smoothly towards the west, till he reached the strand; and when his gold-shod hooves touched the waves, he shook himself and neighed three times. He made no delay, but plunged forward at once, moving over the face of the sea with the speed of a cloud-shadow on a March day. The wind overtook the waves and we overtook the wind, so that we straightway lost sight of land; and we saw nothing but billows tumbling before us and billows tumbling behind us.

Other shores came into view, and we saw many wonderful things on our journey—islands and cities, lime-white mansions, bright grianáns [summer houses] and lofty palaces. A hornless fawn once crossed our course, bounding nimbly along from the crest of one wave to the crest of another; and close after in full chase, a white hound with red ears. We saw also a lovely young maiden on a brown steed, with a golden apple in her hand; and as she passed swiftly by, a young warrior on a white steed plunged after her, wearing a long, flowing mantle of yellow silk, and holding a gold-hilted sword in his hand.

I knew naught of these things, and, marvelling much, I asked the princess what they meant.

"Heed not what you see here, Oisin," she said, "for all these wonders are as nothing compared with what you shall see in Tir na nOg."

At last we saw at a great distance, rising over the waves on the very verge of the sea, a palace more splendid than all the others; and, as we drew near, its front glittered like the morning sun. I asked the lady what royal house this was, and who was the prince that ruled over it.

"This country is the Land of Virtues," she replied. "Its King is the giant, Fomor of the Blows, and its Queen the daughter of the King of the Land of Life. This Fomor brought the lady away by force from her own country, and keeps her in his palace. But she has put him under 'geasa' that he cannot break through, never to ask her to marry him till she can find a champion to fight him in single combat. Yet she still remains in bondage, for no hero has yet come hither who has the courage to meet the giant."

"A blessing on you, golden-haired Niamh," I replied. "I have never heard music sweeter than your voice and although I feel pity for this princess, yet your story is pleasant to hear. Of a certainty I will go to the palace, and try whether I cannot kill this Fomor, and free the lady."

So we came to land, and as we drew nigh to the palace the lovely princess met us and bade us welcome. She led us in and placed us on chairs of gold. After which choice food was placed before us, and drinking-horns filled with mead, and golden goblets of sweet wine.

When we had eaten and drunk, the mild young princess told us her story, while tears streamed from her soft blue eyes. She ended by saying: "I shall never return to my own country and to my father's house, so long as this great and cruel giant is live."

When I heard her sad voice, and saw her tears falling, I was moved with pity. Telling her to cease from her grief, I gave her my hand as a pledge that I would meet the giant, and either slay him or fall myself in her defence.

While we were yet speaking, we saw the giant coming towards the palace, large of body and ugly and hateful in appearance, carrying a load of deerskins on his back and holding a great iron club in his hand. He threw down his load when he saw us, turned a surly look on the princess, and, without greeting us, or showing the least mark of courtesy, he forthwith challenged me to battle in a loud, rough voice.

It was not my wont to be dismayed by a call to battle, or to be terrified at the sight of an enemy, and I went forth at once without the least fear in my heart. But though I had fought many battles in Erin against wild boars and enchanters and foreign invaders, never before did I find it so hard to preserve my life. We fought for three days and three nights without food or drink or sleep, for the giant did not give me a moment for rest and neither did I give him. At length, when I looked at the two princesses weeping in great fear, and when I called to mind my father's deeds in battle, the fury of my valour arose. With a sudden onset I felled the giant to the earth and instantly, before he could recover himself, I cut off his head.

When the maidens saw the monster lying on the ground dead, they uttered three cries of joy and they came to me, and led me into the palace. For I was indeed bruised all over, and covered with gory wounds, and a sudden dizziness of brain and feebleness of body seized me. But the daughter of the King of the Land of Life applied precious balsam and healing herbs to my wounds and in a short time I was healed, and my cheerfulness of mind returned.

Then I buried the giant in a deep and wide grave and I raised a great carn over him, and placed on it a stone with his name graved in Ogham.

We rested that night, and at the dawn of next morning Niamh said to me that it was time for us to resume our journey to Tir na nOg. So we took leave of the daughter of the King of the Land of Life; and though her heart was joyful after her release, she wept at our departure, and we were not less sorry at parting from her. When we had mounted the white steed, he galloped towards the strand. As soon as his hooves touched the wave, he shook himself and neighed three times. We plunged forward over the clear, green sea with the speed of a March wind on a hillside. Soon we saw nothing but billows tumbling before us and billows tumbling behind us. We saw again the fawn chased by the white hound with red ears, and the maiden with the golden apple passed swiftly by, followed by the young warrior in yellow silk on his white steed. And again we passed many strange islands and cities and white palaces.

The sky now darkened, so that the sun was hidden from our view. A storm arose, and the sea was lighted up with constant flashes. But though the wind blew from every point of the heavens, and the waves rose up and roared around us, the white steed kept his course straight on, moving as calmly and swiftly as before, through the foam and blinding spray, without being delayed or disturbed in the least, and without turning either to the right or to the left.

At length the storm abated, and after a time the sun again shone brightly. When I looked up, I saw a country near at hand, all green and full of flowers, with beautiful smooth plains, blue hills, and bright lakes and waterfalls. Not far from the shore stood a palace of surpassing beauty and splendour. It was covered all over with gold and with gems of every colour—blue, green, crimson, and yellow. On each side were grianáns shining with precious stones, built by artists the most skilful that could be found.

I asked Niamh the name of that delightful country, and she replied: "This is my native country, Tir na nOg. And there is nothing I have promised you that you will not find in it."

As soon as we reached the shore, we dismounted; and now we saw advancing from the palace a troop of noble-looking warriors, all clad in bright garments, who came forward to meet and welcome us. Following these we saw a stately glittering host, with the King at their head wearing a robe of bright yellow satin covered with gems, and a crown that sparkled with gold and diamonds. The Queen came after, attended by a hundred lovely young maidens; and as they advanced towards us, it seemed to me that this King and Queen exceeded all the kings and queens of the world in beauty and gracefulness and majesty.

After they had kissed their daughter, the King took my hand, and said aloud in the hearing of the host: "This is Oisin, the son of Finn, for whom my daughter, Niamh, travelled over the sea to Erin. This is Oisin, who is to be the husband of Niamh of the Golden Hair. We give you a hundred thousand welcomes, brave Oisin. You will be forever young in this land. All kinds of delights and innocent pleasures are awaiting you, and my daughter, the gentle, golden-haired Niamh, shall be your wife, for I am King of Tir na nOg."

I gave thanks to the King, and I bowed low to the Queen; after which we went into the palace, where we found a banquet prepared. The feasting and rejoicing lasted for ten days, and on the last day I was wedded to the gentle Niamh of the Golden Hair.

I lived in the Land of Youth more than three hundred years, but it appeared to me that only three years had passed since the day I parted from my friends. At the end of that time, I began to have a longing desire to see my father, Finn, and all my old friends, and I asked leave of Niamh and of the King to visit Erin.

The King gave permission, and Niamh said: "I will give consent, though I feel sorrow in my heart, for I fear much you will never return to me."

I replied that I would surely return, and that she need not feel any doubt or dread, for that the white steed knew the way and would bring me back in safety. Then she addressed me in these words, which seemed very strange to me.

"I will not refuse this request, though your journey afflicts me with great grief and fear. Erin is not now as it was when you left it. The great King Finn and his Fena are all gone. You will find, instead of them, a holy father and hosts of priests and saints. Now, think well on what I say to you, and keep my words in your mind. If once you alight from the white steed, you will never come back to me. Again I warn you, if you place your feet on the green sod in Erin, you will never return to this lovely land. A third time, O Oisin, my beloved husband, a third time I say to you, if you alight from the white steed, you will never see me again."

I promised that I would faithfully attend to her words, and that I would not alight from the white steed. Then, as I looked into her gentle face and marked her grief, my heart was weighed down with sadness, and my tears flowed plentifully. But even so, my mind was bent on coming back to Erin.

When I had mounted the white steed, he galloped straight towards the shore. We moved as swiftly as before over the clear sea. The wind overtook the waves and we overtook the wind, so that we straightway left the Land of Youth behind. We passed by many islands and cities, till at length we landed on the green shores of Erin.

As I travelled on through the country, I looked closely around me, but I scarcely knew the old places, for everything seemed strangely altered. I saw no sign of Finn, and his host, and I began to dread that Niamh's saying was coming true. At length, I espied at a distance a company of little men and woman, all mounted on horses as small as themselves; and when I came near, they greeted me kindly and courteously. They looked at me with wonder and curiosity, and they marvelled much at my great size, and at the beauty and majesty of my person.

I asked them about Finn and the Fena—whether they were still living, or if any sudden disaster had swept them away. And one replied: "We have heard of the hero Finn, who ruled the Fena of Erin in times of old, and who never had an equal for bravery and wisdom. The poets of Gael have written many books concerning his deeds and the deeds of the Fena, which we cannot now relate, but they are gone long since, for they lived many ages ago. We have heard also, and we have seen it written in very old books, that Finn had a son named Oisin. Now this Oisin went with a young fairy maiden to Tir na nOg, and his father and his friends sorrowed greatly after him, and sought him long; but he was never seen again."

When I heard all this, I was filled with amazement, and my heart grew heavy with sorrow. I silently turned my steed from the wondering people, and set forward straightway for Allen of the mighty deeds, on the broad, green plains of Leinster. It was a miserable journey to me; and though my mind, being full of sadness at all I saw and heard, forecasted further sorrows, I was grieved more than ever when I reached Allen. For there, indeed, I found the hill deserted and lonely, and my father's palace all in ruins and overgrown with grass and weeds.

I turned slowly away, and afterwards fared through the land in every direction in search of my friends. But I met only crowds of little people, all strangers, who gazed at me with wonder, and none knew me. I visited every place throughout the country where I knew the Fena had lived, but I found their houses all like Allen, solitary and in ruins and overgrown with grass and weeds.

At length I came to Glenasmole, where many a time I had hunted in days of old with the Fena, and there I saw a crowd of people in the glen.

As soon as they saw me, one of them came forward and said: "Come to us, thou mighty hero, and help us out of our strait, for thou art a man of vast strength."

I went to them, and found a number of men trying in vain to raise a large, flat stone. It was half-lifted from the ground, but those who were under it were not strong enough either to raise it further or to free themselves from its weight. And they were in great distress, and on the point of being crushed to death.

I thought it a shameful thing that so many men should be unable to lift this stone, which Oscar, if he were alive, would take in his right hand and fling over the heads of the feeble crowd. After I had looked a little while, I stooped forward and seized the flag with one hand; and, putting forth my strength, I flung it seven perches from its place, and relieved the little men. But with the great strain the golden saddle-girth broke, and, bounding forward to keep myself from falling, I suddenly came to the ground on my two feet.

The moment the white steed felt himself free, he shook himself and neighed. Then, starting off with the speed of a cloud-shadow on a March day, he left me standing helpless and sorrowful. Instantly a woeful change came over me: the sight of my eyes began to fade, the ruddy beauty of my face fled, I lost all my strength, and I fell to the earth, a poor, withered old man, blind and wrinkled and feeble.

The white steed was never seen again. I never recovered my sight, my youth, or my strength; and I have lived in this manner, sorrowing without ceasing for my gentle, golden-haired wife, Niamh, and thinking ever of my father, Finn, and of the lost companions of my youth.

St. Brigid's Cloak

BY PATRICK KENNEDY

*t*he King of Leinster at that time was not particularly generous, and St. Brigid found it not easy to make him contribute in a respectable fashion to her many charities. One day when he proved more than usually niggardly, she at last said, as it were in jest: "Well, at least grant me as much land as I can cover with my cloak." And, to get rid of her importunity, he consented.

They were at the time standing on the highest point of ground of the Curragh, and she directed four of her sisters to spread out the cloak preparatory to her taking possession. They accordingly took up the garment, but instead of laying it flat on the turf, each virgin, with face turned to a different point of the compass, began to run swiftly, the cloth expanding at their wish in all directions. Other pious ladies, as the border enlarged, seized portions of it to preserve something of a circular shape, and the elastic extension continued till the breadth was a mile at least.

"Oh, St. Brigid," said the frighted King, "what are you about?"

"I am—or rather my cloak is—about to cover your whole province to punish you for your stinginess to the poor."

"Oh! Come! Come! This won't do. Call your maidens back. I will give you a decent plot of ground, and be more liberal for the future."

The saint was easily persuaded, She obtained some acres, and if the King held his purse-strings tight on any future occasion she had only to allude to her cloak's miraculous qualities to bring him to reason.

The Giant's Stairs

BY T. CROFTON CROKER

On the road between Passage and Cork there is an old mansion called Ronayne's Court. It may be easily known from the stack of chimneys and the gable ends, which are to be seen, look at it which way you will. Here it was that Maurice Ronayne and his wife Margaret Gould kept house, as may be learned to this day from the great old chimney-piece, on which is carved their arms. They were a mighty worthy couple, and had but one son, who was called Philip, after no less a person than the King of Spain.

Immediately on his smelling the cold air of this world the child sneezed, which was naturally taken to be a good sign of his having a clear head; and the subsequent rapidity of his learning was truly amazing, for on the very first day a primer was put into his hands he tore out the A, B, C page and destroyed it as a thing quite beneath his notice. No wonder then that both father and mother were proud of their heir, who gave such indisputable proofs of genius, or, as they called it in that part of the world, "genus".

One morning, however, Master Phil, who was then just seven years old, was missing, and no one could tell what had become of him. Servants were sent in all directions to seek him, on horseback and on foot, but they returned without any tidings of the boy, whose disappearance altogether was most unaccountable. A large reward was offered, but it produced them no intelligence, and years rolled away without Mr. and Mrs. Ronayne having obtained any satisfactory account of the fate of their lost child.

There lived at this time, near Carrigaline, one Robin Kelly, a blacksmith by trade. He was what is termed a handyman, and his abilities were held in much estimation by the lads and the lasses of the neighbourhood. For, independent of shoeing horses, which

he did to great perfection, and making plough-irons, he inter-
preted dreams for the young women, sung "Arthur O'Bradley"
at their weddings, and was so good-natured a fellow at a christen-
ing, that he was gossip to half the country round.

Now it happened that Robin had a dream himself, and young
Philip Ronayne appeared to him in it, at the dead hour of the
night. Robin thought he saw the boy mounted upon a beautiful
white horse, and that he told him how he was made a page to the
giant Mahon Mac Mahon, who had carried him off, and who held
his Court in the hard heart of the rock.

"The seven years—my time of service—are clean out, Robin,"
said he. "If you release me this night I will be the making of you
for ever after."

"And how will I know," said Robin—cunning enough, even
in his sleep—"but this is all a dream?"

"Take that," said the boy, "for a token." And at the word the
white horse struck out with one of his hind legs, and gave poor
Robin such a kick in the forehead that, thinking he was a dead
man, he roared as loud as he could after his brains, and woke up
calling a thousand murders. He found himself in bed, but he had
the mark of the blow, the regular print of a horse-shoe upon his
forehead as red as blood. Robin Kelly, who never before found
himself puzzled at the dream of any other person, did not know
what to think of his own.

Robin was well acquainted with the Giant's Stairs—as, indeed,
who is not who knows the harbour? They consist of great masses
of rock, which, piled one above another, rise like a flight of steps
from very deep water, against the bold cliff of Carrigmahon. Nor
are they badly suited for stairs to those who have legs of sufficient
length to stride over a moderate-sized house, or to enable them
to clear the space of a mile in a hop, step, and jump. Both these
feats the giant Mac Mahon was said to have performed in the
days of Finnian glory, and the common tradition of the country
placed his dwelling within the cliff up whose side the stairs led.

Such was the impression which the dream made on Robin, that
he determined to put its truth to the test. It occurred to him,
however, before setting out on this adventure, that a plough-iron
may be no bad companion, as, from experience, he knew it was
an excellent knockdown argument, having on more occasions
than one settled a little disagreement very quietly. So, putting
one on his shoulder, off he marched in the cool of the evening,
through Glaun a Thowk (The Hawk's Glen) to Monkstown.

Here an old gossip of his (Tom Clancey by name) lived, who, on hearing Robin's dream, promised him the use of his skiff, and moreover offered to assist in rowing it to the Giant's Stairs.

After a supper which was of the best, they embarked. It was a beautiful still night, and the little boat glided swiftly along. The regular dip of the oars, the distant song of the sailor, and sometimes the voice of a belated traveller at the ferry of Carrigaloe, alone broke the quietness of the land and sea and sky. The tide was in their favour, and in a few minutes Robin and his gossip rested on their oars under the shadow of the Giant's Stairs.

Robin looked anxiously for the entrance to the Giant's palace, which, it was said, may be found by anyone seeking it at midnight, but no such entrance could he see. His impatience had hurried him there before that time, and after waiting a considerable space in a state of suspense not to be described, Robin, with pure vexation, could not help exclaiming to his companion: " 'Tis a pair of fools we are, Tom Clancey, for coming here at all on the strength of a dream!"

"And whose doing is it," said Tom, "but your own?"

At that moment they perceived a faint glimmering of light to proceed from the cliff, which gradually increased until a porch big enough for a king's palace unfolded itself almost on a level with the water. They pulled the skiff directly towards the opening, and Robin Kelly, seizing his plough-iron, boldly entered with a strong hand and a stout heart.

Wild and strange was that entrance. The whole of it appeared formed of grim and grotesque faces, blending so strangely each with the other that it was impossible to define any. The chin of one formed the nose of another; what appeared to be a fixed and stern eye, if dwelt upon, changed to a gaping mouth; and the lines of the lofty forehead grew into a majestic and flowing beard. The more Robin allowed himself to contemplate the forms around him, the more terrifying they became, and the stony expressions of this crook of faces assumed a savage ferocity as his imagination converted feature after feature into a different shape and character.

Losing the twilight in which these indefinite forms were visible, he advanced through a dark and devious passage, whilst a deep and rumbling noise sounded as if the rock was about to close upon him and swallow him up alive for ever. Now, indeed, poor Robin felt afraid. "Robin, Robin," said he, "if you were a fool for coming here, what in the name of fortune are you now?"

But, as before, he had scarcely spoken, when he saw a small light twinkling through the darkness of the distance, like a star in the midnight sky. To retreat was out of the question because so many turnings and windings were in the passage, that he considered he had but little chance of making his way back. He therefore proceeded towards the bit of light, and came at last into a spacious chamber, from the roof of which hung the solitary lamp that had guided him. Emerging from such profound gloom, the single lamp afforded Robin abundant light to discover several gigantic figures seated round a massive stone table, as if in serious deliberation, but no word disturbed the breathless silence which prevailed.

At the head of this table sat Mahon Mac Mahon himself, whose majestic beard had taken root, and in the course of ages grown into the stone slab. He was the first who perceived Robin, and, instantly starting up, drew his long beard from out the huge piece of rock in such haste and with so sudden a jerk that it was shattered into a thousand pieces.

"What seek you?" he demanded in a voice of thunder.

"I come," answered Robin, with as much boldness as he could put on, for his heart was almost fainting within him, "I come," said he, "to claim Philip Ronayne, whose time of service is out this night."

"And who sent you here?" said the giant.

" 'Twas of my own accord I came," said Robin.

"Then you must single him out from among my pages," said the giant, "and if you fix on the wrong one, you life is forfeit. Follow me."

He led Robin into a hall of vast extent, and filled with lights, along either side of which were rows of beautiful children, all apparently seven years old, and none beyond that age, dressed in green, and every one exactly dressed alike.

"Here," said Mahon, "you are free to take Philip Ronayne, if you will. But remember, I give but one choice."

Robin was sadly perplexed, for there were hundreds of children and he had no very clear recollection of the boy he sought. But he walked along the hall, by the side of Mahon, as if nothing was the matter, although his great iron dress clanked fearfully at every step, sounding louder than Robin's own sledge battering on his anvil.

They had nearly reached the end without speaking, when Robin, seeing that the only means he had was to make friends with the giant, determined to try what effect a few soft words might have.

" 'Tis a fine wholesome appearance the poor children carry," remarked Robin, "although they have been here so long shut out from the fresh air and the blessed light of heaven. 'Tis tenderly your honour must have reared them."

"Ay," said the giant, "that is true for you. So give me your hand—for you are, I believe, a very honest fellow for a blacksmith."

Robin at the first look did not much like the huge size of the hand, and therefore presented his plough-iron which, the giant seizing, twisted in his grasp round and round again as if it had been a potato stalk; on seeing this all the children set up a shout of laughter.

In the midst of their mirth Robin thought he heard his name called. All ear and eye, he put his hand on the boy who he fancied had spoken, crying out at the same time: "Let me live or die for it, but this is young Phil Ronayne."

"It is Philip Ronayne—happy Philip Ronayne," said his young companions; and in an instant the hall became dark. Crashing noises were heard, and all was in strange confusion, but Robin held fast his prize, and found himself lying in the grey dawn of the morning at the head of the Giant's Stairs with the boy clasped in his arms.

Robin had plenty of gossips to spread the story of his wonderful adventure. Passage, Monkstown, Carrigaline—the whole barony of Kerricurrihy rung with it.

"Are you quite sure, Robin, it is young Phil Ronayne you have brought back with you?" was the regular question; for although the boy had been seven years away, his appearance now was just the same as on the day he was missed. He had neither grown taller nor older in look, and he spoke of things which had happened before he was carried off as one awakened from sleep, or as if they had occurred yesterday.

"Am I sure? Well, that's a queer question," was Robin's reply. "Seeing the boy has the blue eyes of his mother, with the foxy hair of the father, to say nothing of the purty wart on the right side of his little nose."

However Robin Kelly may have been questioned, the worthy couple of Ronayne's Court doubted not that he was the deliverer of their child from the power of the giant Mac Mahon; and the reward they bestowed on him equalled their gratitude.

Philip Ronayne lived to be an old man; and he was remarkable to the day of his death for his skill in working brass and iron, which it was believed he had learned during his seven years' apprenticeship to the giant Mahon Mac Mahon.

The Crookened Back

BY T. CROFTON CROKER

Peggy Barrett was once tall, well-shaped and comely. She was in her youth remarkable for two qualities, not often found together, of being the most thrifty housewife, and the best dancer in her native village of Ballyhooley.

But she is now upwards of sixty years old, and during the last ten years of her life she has never been able to stand upright. Her back is bent nearly to a level, yet she has the freest use of all her limbs that can be enjoyed in such a posture. Her health is good and her mind vigorous, and, in the family of her eldest son, with whom she has lived since the death of her husband, she performs all the domestic services which her age, and the infirmity just mentioned, allow. She washes the potatoes, makes the fire, sweeps the house (labours in which she good-humouredly says she finds her crooked back mighty convenient), plays with the children, and tells stories to the family and their neighbouring friends, who often collect round her son's fireside to hear them during the long winter evenings.

Her powers of conversation are highly extolled, both for humour and narration, and anecdotes of droll or awkward incidents, connected with the posture in which she has been so long fixed as well as the history of the occurrence to which she owes that misfortune, are favourite topics of her discourse. Among other matters she is fond of relating how, on a certain day, at the close of a bad harvest, when several tenants of the estate on which she lived concerted in a field a petition for an abatement of rent, they placed the paper on which they wrote upon her back, which was found no very inconvenient substitute for a table.

Peggy, like all experienced story-tellers, suited her tales, both in length and subject, to the audience and the occasion. She knew that, in broad daylight, when the sun shines brightly, and the trees are budding, and the birds singing around us, when men and women like ourselves are moving and speaking, employed variously in business or amusement, when we are engaged about the realities of life and nature, we want that spirit of credulity without which tales of the deepest interest will lose their power. At such times Peggy was brief, very particular as to facts, and never dealt in the marvellous.

But round the blazing hearth of a Christmas evening, when infidelity is banished from all companies, at least in low and simple life, as a quality, to say the least of it, out of season; when the winds of "dark December" whistled bleakly round the walls, and almost through the doors of the little mansion, reminding its inmates that as the world is vexed by elements superior to human power, so it may be visited by beings of a superior nature. At such times would Peggy Barrett give full scope to her memory, or her imagination, or both, and upon one of these occasions she gave the following circumstantial account of the "crookening of her back".

"It was, of all days in the year, the day before May-day, that I went out to the garden to weed the potatoes. I would not have gone out that day but I was dull in myself, and sorrowful, and wanted to be alone. All the boys and girls were laughing and joking in the house, making goaling-balls and dressing out ribbons for the mummers next day. I couldn't bear it.

" 'Twas only at the Easter that was then past (and that's ten years last Easter—I won't forget the time), that I buried my poor man. I thought how gay and joyful I was, many a long year before that, at the May-eve before our wedding, when with Robin by my side I sat cutting and sewing the ribbons for the goaling-ball I was to give the boys on the next day, proud to be preferred above all the other girls of the banks of the Blackwater by the handsomest boy and the best hurler in the village.

"So I left the house and went to the garden. I stayed there all day, and didn't come home to dinner. I don't know how it was but somehow I continued on, weeding and thinking sorrowfully enough, and singing over some of the old songs that I sung many and many a time in the days that are gone, and for them that never will come back to me to hear them. The truth is, I hated to go and sit silent and mournful among the people in the house, that were merry and young, and had the best of their days before them.

" 'Twas late before I thought of returning home, and I did not leave the garden till some time after sunset. The moon was up, but though there wasn't a cloud to be seen, and though a star was winking here and there in the sky, the day wasn't long enough gone to have it clear moonlight. Still it shone enough to make everything on one side of the heavens look pale and silvery-like, and the thin white mist was just beginning to creep along the fields. On the other side, near where the sun was set, there was more of day-light, and the sky looked angry, red, and fiery through the trees, like as if it was lighted up by a great town burning below. Everything was as silent as a churchyard, only now and then one could hear far off a dog barking, or a cow lowing after being milked. There wasn't a creature to be seen on the road or in the fields.

"I wondered at this first, but then I remembered it was May-eve, and that many a thing, both good and bad, would be wandering about that night, and that I ought to shun danger as well as others. So I walked on as quick as I could, and soon came to the end of the demesne wall, where the trees rise high and thick at each side of the road, and almost meet at the top. My heart misgave me when I got under the shade. There was so much light let down from the opening above that I could see about a stone-throw before me.

"All of a sudden I heard a rustling among the branches, on the right side of the road, and saw something like a small black goat, only with long wide horns turned out instead of being bent backwards, standing upon its hind legs upon the top of the wall, and looking down on me. My breath was stopped, and I couldn't move for near a minute. I couldn't help, somehow, keeping my eyes fixed on it, and it never stirred but kept looking in the same fixed way down at me.

"I made a rush, and went on; but I didn't go ten steps when I saw the very same sight on the wall, to the left of me, standing in exactly the same manner, but three or four times as high, and almost as tall as the tallest man. The horns looked frightful. It gazed upon me as before; my legs shook, my teeth chattered, and I thought I would drop down dead every moment.

"At last I felt as if I was obliged to go on, and on I went, but it was without feeling how I moved, or whether my legs carried me. Just as I passed the spot where this frightful thing was standing, I heard a noise as if something sprung from the wall, and felt as if a heavy animal plumped down upon me, and held with the fore-feet clinging to my shoulders, and the hind ones fixed in my gown, that was folded and pinned up behind me. 'Tis

the wonder of my life ever since how I bore the shock, but so it was.

"I neither fell, nor even staggered with the weight, but walked on as if I had the strength of ten men, though I felt as if I couldn't help moving, and couldn't stand still if I wished it. Though I gasped with fear, I knew as well as I do now what I was doing. I tried to cry out, but couldn't. I tried to run, but wasn't able. I tried to look back, but my head and neck were as if they were screwed in a vice. I could barely roll my eyes on each side, and then I could see, as clearly and plainly as if it was in the broad light of the blessed sun, a black and cloven foot planted upon each of my shoulders. I heard a low breathing in my ear. I felt, at every step I took, my leg strike back against the feet of the creature that was on my back. Still I could do nothing but walk straight on.

"Now I came within sight of the house, and a welcome sight it was to me, for I thought I would be released when I reached it. I soon came close to the door, but it was shut to, for they were more cautious about May-eve than I was. I saw the light inside, through the chinks of the door. I heard 'em talking and laughing within. I felt myself at three yards' distance from them that would die to save me. May the Lord save me from ever again feeling what I did that night, when I found myself held by what couldn't be good nor friendly, but without the power to help myself, or to call my friends, or to put out my hand to knock, or even to lift my leg to strike the door, and let them know that I was outside. 'Twas as if my hands grew to my sides, and my feet were glued to the ground, or had the weight of a rock fixed to them.

"Then I thought of blessing myself, and my right hand, that would do nothing else, did that for me. Still the weight remained on my back, and all was as before. I blessed myself again: 'twas still all the same. I then gave myself up for lost: but I blessed myself a third time, and my hand no sooner finished the sign, than all at once I felt the burthen spring off of my back. The door flew open as if a clap of thunder burst it, and I was pitched forward on my forehead in upon the middle of the floor. When I got up my back was crookened, and I never stood straight from that night to this blessed hour."

There was a pause when Peggy Barrett finished. Those who had heard the story before had listened with a look of half-satisfied interest, blended, however, with an expression of that serious and solemn feeling which always attends a tale of supernatural wonders, how ever often told. They moved upon their seats out of the posture in which they had remained fixed during the narrative, and sat in an attitude which denoted that their curiosity as to the cause of this strange occurrence had been long since allayed. Those to whom it was before unknown still retained their look and posture of strained attention, and anxious but solemn expectation.

A grandson of Peggy's, about nine years old (not the child of the son with whom she lived), had never before heard the story. As it grew in interest, he was observed to cling closer and closer to the old woman's side, and at the close he was gazing steadfastly at her, with his body bent back across her knees, and his face turned up to hers, with a look through which a disposition to weep seemed contending with curiosity. After a moment's pause he could no longer restrain his impatience, and catching her grey locks in one hand, while the tear of dread and wonder was just dropping from his eyelash, he cried: "Granny, what was it?"

The old woman smiled first at the elder part of her audience, and then at her grandson, and patting him on the forehead, she said: "It was the Pooka."

Great Fairy Tales
of Ireland

Contents

	PAGE
INTRODUCTION	5
JAMIE FREEL AND THE YOUNG LADY *Letitia Maclintock*	9
THE FAIRIES *William Allingham*	15
HIE OVER TO ENGLAND *Retold by Mary McGarry*	18
THE CAPTIVE PIPER *Retold by Mary McGarry*	25
TWO TALES OF LEPRECHAUNS *Introduction by Mary McGarry*	29
THE MAGIC SHILLING *Retold by Mary McGarry*	30
THE LEPRECHAUN OF CARRIGADHROID *Retold by Mary McGarry*	33
THE PHOUKA *Lady Wilde*	40
FAIR, BROWN, AND TREMBLING *Joseph Jacobs*	43
THE WELL OF D'YERREE-IN-DOWAN *Douglas Hyde*	52
COUNTRY-UNDER-WAVE *Alice Furlong*	63
THE ENCHANTED ISLAND *Anonymous*	76

(continued overleaf)

THE FAIRY TREE
Retold by Mary McGarry   77

THE FAIRY THORN
Sir Samuel Ferguson   83

THE SON OF BAD COUNSEL
Retold by Mary McGarry   86

THE LADY OF GOLLERUS
T. Crofton Croker   92

THE WHITE HEN
Retold by Mary McGarry   99

THE WHITE FAIRY HORSE
Dermott MacManus   109

EDAIN THE QUEEN
Lady Wilde   112

EARL DESMOND AND THE BANSHEE
Anonymous   116

THE HARP OF THE DAGDA MOR
Alice Furlong   119

A SELECT BIBLIOGRAPHY   127

Introduction

*t*he fairy faith is reflected in both the folklore and the written traditions of Ireland. Who are these fairies? They are not the colourful characters of pantomimes nor do they bear much resemblance to the fantasies of Walt Disney. They are simply the 'little people', who for centuries were an accepted feature of country life. Though most are diminutive beings, others can appear as fully grown men and women and intermingle naturally in human society.

Our fairylore includes a wide range of beliefs about the souls of the dead, pagan deities and spirits, kindly and malevolent. It centres round the many *raths* or hillforts that are still to be seen on the Irish landscape. These mounds, some with curious underground passages and prehistoric burial chambers, became inextricably linked in the popular imagination with the realm of the unknown, the world of faery. Mythology associated the fairies with the ancient race of the Tuatha De Danann, known to have been adepts in sorcery and magic. When conquered by later invaders, the Milesians, they are said to have withdrawn to live in immortality in the hills, caves and waters of Ireland. In Gaelic the fairies are always referred to as the *sidhe*, the people of the mounds.

In Christian times it has been commonly held by country people that the fairies are fallen angels. These spirits that remained neutral in the revolt by Satan were not condemned to hell. Nevertheless they could not be allowed to remain in the Heavenly Kingdom since they had failed to prove their loyalty. They were therefore banished to earth, there to dwell beneath the grassy hillsides and the waves of the ocean until the day of judgement. It is said that St. Columcille was once asked whether the fairy host could hope for salvation on the Last Day; he sadly replied that when that time arrived they would be finally doomed. Maybe this explains the strange mixture of good and evil that is so evident in these mystical creatures.

Beneath the popular explanations of the phenomena lies the suggestion of one central idea permeating the whole fairy tradition. Is this to be found in the vast body of mystic thought, the close resemblence between the old Celtic doctrine of re-birth, and the belief of Eastern religions in the unknown regions of the sub-conscious? Strong claims have been made also for the existence of psychic entities quite distinct from the ghosts or shades of the dead.

Many fairy tales involve the leading personages of the De-dananns, who appear to have assumed god-like qualities in the transformation of the race. Mananann Mac Lir is an Irish sea-god or Neptune, who rules over an oceanic fairyland often called 'The Country-Under-Wave' or *Tir-Faoi-Thonn* – he may also have given his name to the Isle of Man. The legend of a beautiful land situated under the sea has the character of a Gaelic 'Atlantis', an enchanted island sunk at some remote time and still under spell. On a fine day one can supposedly catch a glimpse of the rooftops and turrets of this amazing realm, the *Hy-Brasail* of the poets.

Aine, the fairy queen in the tale of the 'Captive Piper' is the sub-ject of much folklore in the province of Munster. Like other Dedan-ann figures she was closely connected with ideas of fertility and increase – the Hill of Aine, Knockaney was for a long time a place of vigil on Midsummer's Eve. The Dagda was the father and chief of the Dedananna, the musician whose harp had the power to enchant and hypnotize. It was one of his sons, Midar the Proud, who fell in love with the mortal Queen Edain.

Superstitions about the fairies abound. To disturb a fairy rath is to risk the retribution of the elfin race. If your house lies on a 'fairy path' at certain times of the year you must leave your doors open to allow the invisible cavalcade to pass through. The only indication of their passage is the rush of fairy wind. The great lords of Ireland long ago used to leave a keg of their best Spanish wine on the window sill for the fairies – the following morning it would always be gone. The fairies appreciate these small cour-tesies and are greatly offended if a small part of our human fare is not offered to them.

All our accounts of the fairies show that they are an artistic people that love beauty, music and pleasure. The romantic dells and woods they choose for their midnight revels are known to locals as the 'gentle places'. Here their tiny dancing feet leave scorched 'fairy-rings' on the grass. The hawthorn is the shrub around which they gather for their merrymaking. Their music is said to remain forever in the soul of the mortal eavesdropper and many fine old Irish tunes are reputed to have come from fairy airs. Carolan, the great Gaelic bard, so the story goes, fell asleep on a rath and ever afterwards the haunting music of the fairies inspired his compositions.

An interest in human affairs and especially individual mortals is characteristic of the fairy race. Sometimes this involvement was welcomed – for their knowledge of herbs and potions could cure the ill and bring happiness to the sorrowful. But *pishogues* or fairy spells are often more disruptive than helpful. During the old Celtic festival of *Samhain,* usually referred to as Hallowe'en, fairy power was at its greatest and people were very wary of strange occurrences. Wives and sweethearts were often spirited away to be returned a year later or within seven years, provided they had not eaten or drunk any fairy food. Frequently a corpse resembling the abducted person was left behind so that the family presumed the absent one to be dead. Parents kept a close watch on an attractive new born child lest the fairies should replace it with an old and wizened changeling. Sprigs of mistletoe, branches of mountain ash and fire and iron were all thought to afford protection against such mischief.

There exist two main groups within the fairy world: the trooping and the solitary fairies. The former includes those elfin bands alluded to by Allingham in his poem, 'Up the Airy Mountain'. In order to go hunting or migrate from one place to another they merely get astride rushes or some of the *Buachalan Bui** which are at once transformed into tiny steeds. The Irish merrow is similar to the mermaid and the seal people in that she can discard her fish skin and come ashore to marry a human. Though she may live quite happily in this way for several years and become the mother of earthly children, eventually she is drawn back to the sea, usually by unexpectedly coming across her old skin which fills her with nostalgia for her former way of life.

Among the solitary fairies is the well known leprechaun and the *cluricaun,* a tiny household sprite. The pooka, a spirit which assumes animal form, often that of a horse, and the banshee, a female harbinger of death that attaches itself to certain families would also come into this category. In Ulster the *grogach* is very similar to the pixie or brownie and like the pooka he disappears when rewarded for a good deed. Ireland is not without some of the more frightening creatures of fairy tales. In many parts of the country the term *gruagach* is applied to giants, while the *piasts* are serpents of the lakes, many of whom were destroyed by the great

*Ragwort

Finn Mac Cumhail.

Are fairies as common as they were a hundred years ago? In 'Traces of the Elder Faiths of Ireland' published in 1902, W. G. Wood-Martin wrote:

'On the night of 5th January, the Feast of St. Ceera, the fairies used to hold high revel throughout the length and breadth of Erin. Their last great assembly was in the year 1839, when violent disputes arose among prominent fairy leaders and, the night following, a large portion of the fairy host quitted the Green Isle, never to return. The hurricane they raised in the flight was long referred to by the peasantry as the "Night of the Big Wind".'

But 'seeings' are still reported by many people. Large black dogs which mysteriously vanish from sight are said to be the pooka; if butter or milk disappers in unusual circumstances it is the work of fairies. 'The Middle Kingdom' by Dermot MacManus gives a series of such recent encounters with the 'little people'.

For this collection I have chosen a variety of fairy tales and tales of the fairies. Included are 'wonder' stories, fairy legends, local folklore about the Other World and one tale which is an Irish variant on the international theme of Cinderella – 'Fair, Brown and Trembling' by Joseph Jacobs. Some of the stories I have retold, replacing out-of-date idiom and language and generally making them more readable for the modern audience, though I hope that the essential atmosphere of each is still preserved.

Of the many people who helped me along the way I would particularly like to thank the librarians in Belfast City Library, the National Library of Ireland and Dublin City Library, Pearse Street, and Des Kenny of the Antiquarian Bookshop, Galway. I am very grateful to Dermott MacManus for permission to include 'The White Fairy Horse'.

The simplicity and magic of the fairytale have an appeal for all ages. The interplay of the visible and unseen worlds captures the imagination. Who is to say where reality begins or ends?

Jamie Freel and the Young Lady
A DONEGAL TALE
BY LETITIA MACLINTOCK

Own in Fannet, in times gone by, lived Jamie Freel and his mother. Jamie was the widow's sole support; his strong arm worked for her untiringly, and as each Saturday night came around, he poured his wages into her lap, thanking her dutifully for the halfpence which she returned him for tobacco.

He was extolled by his neighbours as the best son ever known or heard of. But he had neighbours of whose opinion he was ignorant – neighbours who lived pretty close to him, whom he had never seen, who are, indeed, rarely seen by mortals, except on May eves and Halloweens.

An old ruined castle, about a quarter of a mile from his cabin, was said to be the abode of the 'wee folk'. Every Halloween were the ancient windows lighted up, and passers-by saw little figures flitting to and fro inside the building, while they heard the music of pipes and flutes.

It was well known that fairy revels took place; but nobody had the courage to intrude on them.

Jamie had often watched the little figures from a distance, and listened to the charming music, wondering what the inside of the castle was like; but one Halloween he got up and took his cap, saying to his mother, 'I'm awa' to the castle to seek my fortune.'

'What!' cried she, 'would you venture there? You that's the poor widow's own son! Dinna be sae venturesome an' foolitch, Jamie! They'll kill you, an' then what'll come o' me?'

'Never fear, mother; nae harm 'ill happen me, but I maun gae.'

He set out, and as he crossed the potato-field, came in sight of the castle, whose windows were ablaze with light, that seemed to turn the russet leaves, still clinging to the crabtree branches, into gold.

Halting in the grove at one side of the ruin, he listened to the elfin revelry, and the laughter and singing made him all the more determined to proceed.

9

Numbers of little people, the largest about the size of a child of five years old, were dancing to the music of flutes and fiddles, while others drank and feasted.

'Welcome, Jamie Freel! welcome, Jamie!' cried the company, perceiving their visitor. The word 'welcome' was caught up and repeated by every voice in the castle.

Time flew, and Jamie was enjoying himself very much, when his hosts said, 'We're going to ride to Dublin to-night to steal a young lady. Will you come too, Jamie Freel?'

'Ay, that I will! cried the rash youth, thirsting for adventure.

A troop of horses stood at the door. Jamie mounted, and his steed rose with him into the air. He was presently flying over his mother's cottage, surrounded by the elfin troop, and on and on they went, over bold mountains, over little hills, over the deep Lough Swilley, over towns and cottages, when people were burning nuts, and eating apples, and keeping merry Halloween. It seemed to Jamie that they flew all round Ireland before they got to Dublin.

'This is Derry', said the fairies, flying over the cathedral spire; and what was said by one voice was repeated by all the rest, till fifty little voices were crying out, 'Derry! Derry! Derry!'

In like manner was Jamie informed as they passed over each town on the route, and at length he heard the silvery voices cry, 'Dublin! Dublin!'

It was no mean dwelling that was to be honoured by the fairy visit, but one of the finest houses in Stephen's Green.

The troop dismounted near a window, and Jamie saw a beautiful face, on a pillow in a splendid bed. He saw the young lady lifted and carried away, while the stick which was dropped in her place on the bed took her exact form.

The lady was placed before one rider and carried a short way, then given to another, and the names of the towns were cried out as before.

They were approaching home. Jamie heard 'Rathmullan,' 'Milford,' 'Tamney,' and then he knew they were near his own house.

'You've all had your turn at carrying the young lady,' said he. 'Why wouldn't I get her for a wee piece?'

'Ay, Jamie,' replied they, pleasantly, 'you may take your turn at carrying her, to be sure.'

Holding his prize very tightly, he dropped down near his mother's door.

'Jamie Freel, Jamie Freel! is that the way you treat us?' cried they, and they too dropped down near the door.

Jamie held fast, though he knew not what he was holding, for the little folk turned the lady into all sorts of strange shapes. At one moment she was a black dog, barking and trying to bite; at another, a glowing bar of iron, yet without heat; then, again, a sack of wool.

But still Jamie held her, and the baffled elves were turning away, when a tiny woman, the smallest of the party, exclaimed, 'Jamie Freel has her awa' frae us, but he sall hae nae gude o' her, for I'll mak' her deaf and dumb', and she threw something over the young girl.

While they rode off disappointed, Jamie lifted the latch and went in.

'Jamie, man!' cried his mother, 'you've been awa' all night; what have they done on you?'

'Naething bad, mother; I ha' the very best of gude luck. Here's a beautiful young lady I ha' brought you for company.'

'Bless us an' save us!' exclaimed the mother, and for some minutes she was so astonished that she could not think of anything else to say.

Jamie told his story of the night's adventure, ending by saying, 'Surely you wouldna have allowed me to let her gang with them to be lost forever?'

'But a lady, Jamie! How can a lady eat we'er poor diet, and live in we'er poor way? I ax you that, you foolitch fellow?'

'Weel, mother, sure it's better for her to be here nor over yonder,' and he pointed in the direction of the caasle.

Meanwhile, the deaf and dumb girl shivered in her light clothing, stepping close to the humble turf fire.

'Poor crathur, she's quare and handsome! Nae wonder they set their hearts on her,' said the old woman, gazing at her guest with pity and admiration. 'We maun dress her first; but what, in the name o' fortune, hae I fit for the likes o' her to wear?'

She went to the press in 'the room', and took out her Sunday gown of brown drugget; she then opened a drawer, and drew forth a pair of white stockings, a long snowy garment of fine inen, and a cap, her 'dead dress', as she called it.

These articles of attire had long been ready for a certain triste ceremony, in which she would some day fill the chief part, and only saw the light occasionally, when they were hung out to air, but she was willing to give even these to the fair trembling visitor, who was turning in dumb sorrow and wonder from her to Jamie, and from Jamie back to her.

The poor girl suffered herself to be dressed, and then sat down on a 'creepie' in the chimney corner, and buried her face in her hands.

'What'll we do to keep up a lady like thou?' cried the old woman.

'I'll work for you both, mother,' replied her son.

'An' how could a lady live on we'er poor diet?' she repeated.

'I'll work for her,' was all Jamie's answer.

He kept his word. The young lady was very sad for a long time, and tears stole down her cheeks many an evening while the old woman spun by the fire, and Jamie made salmon nets, an accomplishment lately acquired by him, in hopes of adding to the comfort of his guest.

But she was always gentle, and tried to smile when she perceived them looking at her; and by degrees she adapted herself to their ways and mode of life. It was not very long before she began to feed the pig, mash potatoes and meal for the fowls, and knit blue worsted socks.

So a year passed, and Halloween came round again.

'Mother,' said Jamie, taking down his cap, 'I'm off to the ould castle to seek my fortune.'

'Are you mad, Jamie?' cried his mother, in terror; 'sure they'll kill you this time for what you done on them last year.'

Jamie made light of her fears and went his way.

As he reached the crab-tree grove, he saw bright lights in the castle windows as before, and heard loud talking. Creeping under the window, he heard the wee folk say, 'That was a poor trick Jamie Freel payed us this night last year, when he stole the nice young lady from us.'

'Ay,' said the tiny woman, 'an' I punished him for it, for there she sits, a dumb image by his hearth; but he does na' know that three drops o' this glass I hold in my hand wad gie her her hearing and her speeches back again.'

Jamie's heart beat fast as he entered the hall. Again he was greeted by a chorus of welcomes from the company – 'Here comes Jamie Freel! Welcome, welcome, Jamie!'

As soon as the tumult subsided, the little woman said, 'You be to drink our health, Jamie, out o' this glass in my hand.'

Jamie snatched the glass from her hand and darted to the door. He never knew how he reached his cabin, but he arrived there breathless, and sank on a stone by the fire.

'You're kilt surely this time, my poor boy,' said his mother.

'No, indeed, better luck than ever this time!' and he gave the lady three drops of the liquid that still remained at the bottom of the glass, notwithstanding his mad race over the potato-field.

The lady began to speak, and her first words were words of thanks to Jamie.

The three inmates of the cabin had so much to say to one another, that long after cock-crow, when the fairy music had quite ceased, they were talking round the fire.

'Jamie,' said the lady, 'be pleased to get me paper and pen and ink, that I may write to my father, and tell him what has become of me.'

She wrote, but weeks passed, and she received no answer. Again and again she wrote, and still no answer.

At length she said. 'You must come with me to Dublin, Jamie, to find my father.'

'I ha' no money to hire a car for you,' he replied, 'an' how can you travel to Dublin on your foot?'

But she implored him so much that he consented to set out with her, and walk all the way from Fannet to Dublin. It was not as easy as the fairy journey; but at last they rang the bell at the door of the house in Stephen's Green.

'Tell my father that his daughter is here,' said she to the servant who opened the door.

'The gentleman that lives here has no daughter, my girl. He had one, but she died better nor a year ago.'

'Do you not know me, Sullivan?'

'No, poor girl, I do not.'

'Let me see the gentleman. I only ask to see him.'

'Well, that's not much to ax; we'll see what can be done.'

In a few moments the lady's father came to the door.

'Dear father,' said she 'don't you know me?'

'How dare you call me your father?' cried the old gentleman, angrily. 'You are an impostor. I have no daughter.'

'Look in my face, father, and surely you'll remember me.'

'My daughter is dead and buried. She died a long, long time ago.' The old gentleman's voice changed from anger to sorrow. 'You can go,' he concluded.

'Stop, dear father, till you look at this ring on my finger. Look at your name and mine engraved on it.'

'It certainly is my daughter's ring; but I do not know how you came by it. I fear in no honest way.'

'Call my mother, she will be sure to know me,' said the poor girl, who, by this time, was crying bitterly.

'My poor wife is beginning to forget her sorrow. She seldom speaks of her daughter now. Why should I renew her grief by reminding her of her loss?'

But the young lady persevered, till at last the mother was sent for.

'Mother,' she began, when the old lady came to the door, 'Don't you know your daughter?'

'I have no daughter; my daughter died and was buried a long, long time ago.'

'Only look in my face, and surely you'll know me.'

The old lady shook her head.

'You have all forgotten me; but look at this mole on my neck. Surely, mother, you know me now?'

'Yes, yes,' said the mother, 'my Gracie had a mole on her neck like that; but then I saw her in her coffin, and saw the lid shut down upon her.'

It became Jamie's turn to speak, and he gave the history of the fairy journey, of the theft of the young lady, of the figure he had seen laid in its place, of her life with his mother in Fannet, of last Halloween, and of the three drops that had released her from her enchantment.

She took up the story when he paused, and told how kind the mother and son had been to her.

The parents could not make enough of Jamie. They treated him with every distinction, and when he expressed his wish to return to Fannet, said they did not know what to do to show their gratitude.

But an awkward complication arose. The daughter would not let him go without her. 'If Jamie goes, I'll go too,' she said 'He saved me from the fairies, and has worked for me ever since. If it had not been for him, dear father and mother, you would never have seen me again. If he goes, I'll go too.'

This being her resolution, the old gentleman said that Jamie should become his son-in-law. The mother was brought from Fannet in a coach and four, and there was a splendid wedding.

They all lived together in the grand Dublin house, and Jamie was heir to untold wealth at his father-in-law's death.

'The Fairies'

BY WILLIAM ALLINGHAM

Up the airy mountain,
    Down the rushy glen,
We daren't go a-hunting
    For fear of little men;
Wee folk, good folk,
    Trooping all together;
Green jacket, red cap,
    An white owl's feather!

Down along the rocky shore
    Some make their home,
They live on crispy pancakes
    Of yellow tide-foam;
Some in the reeds
    Of the black mountain lake,
With frogs for their watch-dogs
    All night awake.

High on the hill-top
    The old King sits;
He is now so old and gray
    He's nigh lost his wits.
With a bridge of white mist
    Columbkill he crosses,
On his stately journeys
    From Slieveleague to Rosses;
Or going up with music
    On cold starry nights,
To sup with the Queen
    Of the gay Northern Lights.

They stole little Bridget
  For seven years long;
When she came down again
  Her friends were all gone.
They took her lightly back,
  Between the night and morrow,
They thought that she was fast asleep,
  But she was dead with sorrow.
They have kept her ever since
  Deep within the lake,
On a bed of flag-leaves,
  Watching till she wake.

By the craggy hill-side,
  Through the mosses bare,
They have planted thorn-trees
  For pleasure here and there.
Is any man so daring
  As dig them up in spite,
He shall find their sharpest thorns
  In his bed at night.

Up the airy mountain,
  Down the rushy glen,
We daren't go a-hunting
  For fear of little men;
Wee folk, good folk,
  Trooping all together;
Green jacket, red cap,
  And white owl's feather!

Hie Over to England

RETOLD BY MARY McGARRY

One summer in the middle of the last century, an honest and industrious mason named Sean Long, or Jack the Sailor as he spent some time at sea, was employed in building a house not very far from the city of Dublin. As a man who worked hard to earn his living, he normally slept easily and soundly. But one night in the month of July, Sean was awoken by loud talking and sounds of mirth in the kitchen of his small cabin.

Peeping out from his little bedroom, he was startled to discover his kitchen bathed in the most magical aura of light, and a group of tiny figures collected round his hearth before a blazing fire. Little ladies and gentlemen were merrily discussing the merits of sundry bottles of superior whiskey and several jugs of punch. 'Hot, strong and sweet', the exquisite aroma floated up to where Sean stood wonderingly in the half-open doorway. The whole company was attired in very fine, if slightly old-fashioned, clothes; the ladies in golden robes, the gentlemen in wigs and cocked hats.

Now Sean Long was not a man to be easily intimidated. Few would prove stronger than he in a trial of strength and he was ready to meet the stoutest with fist or shillelah. Yet never before had he been confronted by such a scene. 'What sort of a "how-do-you-do" is this?' he whispered to himself. Just at this precise moment one of the gentlemen rose from his seat and, taking off his cocked hat, he put on a red night-cap. The little man then dipped the middle finger of his left hand into a glittering saucer which stood on the mantlepiece and anointed his forehead. Then, addressing the following words to his companions:

> 'Pick up, pick up all your crumbs,
> But touch nothing with your thumbs –
> Hie over to England,'

he vanished from sight.

Next a lady stood up, replaced her rich lace bonnet with a red

cap and picked up some fragments of barnback and saffron cake on which they had been feasting. Brushing her forehead, she repeated the following:

> 'Thus I pick up all my crumbs,
> But touch nothing with my thumbs –
> Hie over to England,'

and disappeared likewise.

Meanwhile poor Sean, too surprised to move an inch, stood as if mesmerized by the events taking place before him. He watched as the whole company passed away, one after the other, male and female alternately, following the same ceremony and repeating the same words, until only one lady and gentleman were left behind. These two looked carefully about to see if all the crumbs were picked up. The lady then said:

> 'We have picked up all our crumbs,
> We've touched nothing with our thumbs;
> Therefore we now may safely say,
> Hie o'er to England – hie away,'

and off she flew.

Finally the last gentleman donned his red cap and having touched his brow, said:

> 'I must now the saucer take,
> Lest I should Sean Long awake;
> Then in his head the whim might rise
> To seize on me, and win the prize.'

Suddenly Sean could restrain himself no longer. Up he jumped and, diving towards the little creature he seized the saucer. But the tiny fellow was too quick for him and rapidly repeating the words, 'Hie over to England', he too vanished before him.

Sean was left holding the saucer in the centre of a room, now dark and silent save for the glow from the turf fire. Disappointment rose in him when he thought how near he had been to pinning a fairy, who might have given his captor wealth and riches to gain his release. 'Maybe,' he mused to himself, 'the prize he was talking about was the saucer – it is a nice bit of china. But I wonder what would happen if I dipped my finger too. I'll try – for I might be lucky, and besides my night-cap is red just like those of the fairies.'

So excited was Sean that he completely forgot that he was

hardly dressed for travelling, being still in his night-shirt. In haste to be off he dipped his finger into the magic saucer, and brushed his forehead. But nothing happened. Then he mocked himself for forgetting to pronounce the words of the spell, and began to sing in a loud voice, 'Hie over to England'. At that he went up through the chimney like a ray of lightning without a touch of bother to himself. His swift journey lulled him into a deep and pleasant slumber.

On awakening he found himself in complete darkness. All the occurrences of the past night he discounted as a mere dream and began to feel about him for all the familiar objects of his home. You can imagine his surprise then to find that he was lying on a heap of saw-dust and that bottles were scattered on either side of him. Investigating his surroundings further, he pushed his head into a hole like a dog-kennel – long, narrow and built with bricks. At once his knowledge of building told him he was in a wine-cellar bin.

'In heaven's name, where am I at all?' he gasped. 'These thieving fairies are after playing the very puck with me, because I disturbed them in their drink. Cooped up like a cracked bottle I am and goodness knows how I'll get out.' His moans met with no response and he chided himself again for acting the 'amadan'* and interfering with the fun of the 'good people'.

Sean remained a long time in the dark cellar, shivering with the cold. The more he thought about it, the harder he found it to believe what had happened was not just a dream. Maybe it was all a practical joke. 'Jack O'Hara' he called out, as it was the name of a mischievous friend, 'there's a good lad, don't be humbugging, but let us out – this is some of your tricks and playacting. Come on, stop your nonsense and let me out.'

The bolt of a door sprang back and a gleam of daylight fell on the shouting figure. A man with a powdered head and dressed in black from head to toe appeared above him followed by a servant in splendid livery with a wine cooper in his hand.

In a wave of relief Sean welcomed them in jovial terms. 'Good luck to you, your honour, and its myself that's glad to see you, but it was too bad of you to leave me here perishing with the cold all this long time.'

'Who have we got here?' was the only reply. 'James, seize that fellow. Now we know who robbed the cellar. No doubt he has

*Gaelic for 'fool'.

a set of false keys hidden on him somewhere.'

Before he knew what to think Sean was seized by several servants, who hurried up at the butler's command, and hauled him out of the cellar. Unfortunately for him he had been apprehended in the house of a certain Lancashire nobleman, from whose cellar a considerable amount of wine had disappeared in a most unaccountable manner. More than one servant had been blamed and dismissed, but now to the joy of all it was believed the real thief had been found. Sean was produced as an object of curiosity in the servants' quarters. No one doubted his guilt or long success in raiding the cellar.

Sounds of the commotion below stairs reached the Earl, who came to inspect the culprit. On appraising Sean's attire, he commented that it was an odd sort of dress he was wearing to commit a robbery in. Poor Sean was no less dismayed at his appearance in the presence of all the world and a lord no less.

'Who are you?' asked his lordship.

'Sean Long, the mason, or otherwise Jack the Sailor at your service', said Sean.

'How can you explain your presence in my cellar?'

'Now that's just what I am trying to figure out myself – I can't make it out at all. But I'll tell you all I know about it, your lordship.'

At this point the housekeeper interrupted to say that the ladies of the house were coming down to hear the story and would it not be a little indiscreet to leave the fellow in his present state. Agreeing with this advice, the Earl commanded the butler to fetch some clothes for the intruder. Soon Sean stood before them, a 'burly groom' in various oddments of stable dress.

'Now,' said the Earl, 'let us hear how you came to be in the cellar.'

Sean described in great detail all that had happened the previous evening; he did not appear in the least disturbed by the shouts of laughter that broke out all around him. And why should he have been, for he was telling the truth, however incredible it seemed to his audience.

'You have a poetic imagination, Sean Long,' said his lordship, 'and if your tale is believed by a jury, it is more than I would credit. My cellar is not the only one which has been robbed. I advise you to admit your guilt and give evidence to the court concerning your accomplices. It is the only hope you have of easing your sentence.'

When Sean protested his innocence he was accused of being an impudent and bare-faced villain and was taken before the local magistrate. Here he met with little more sympathy. The Justice listened with extreme patience to his long and curious story, and when he finished merely turned up his eyes, shrugged his shoulders and ordered the clerk to make out the commital.

'Is it for breaking into the cellar or house of his lordship?' asked the clerk, 'for it has not been ascertained how he got in.'

'For feloniously entering the dwelling', said the Justice emphatically.

Sean was returned to prison to await trial the following day. There in court he repeated his strange account and was treated with contempt by all except for a few who thought he was completely mad. The jury found him guilty and he was sentenced to be hanged the day but one following.

The poor mason's final hour rapidly approached and he was placed in a cart to be carried to the gallows hill. He sat in silence, resigned to meet his death, for it seemed that nothing could save him. As the cart jogged along an old woman standing on the wayside attracted his attention by waving a red cap madly in the air above the heads of the rest of the crowd.

'Sean Long' she cried, 'die with your red night-cap on you, but don't touch it with your thumbs.'

A spark of hope rose in him, but disappeared when he realized he had left his cap behind him in the gaol. The cart reached its destination. The sheriff asked him if he had any last words. Sean took his opportunity and said how much he would like to take his final sleep in his own red night-cap. His request was granted and the cap sent for. While the hangman waited to throw the noose over his head, Sean carefully put on the cap, remembering not to touch it with his thumbs and rubbing his forehead with his middle finger, exclaimed,

'Hie over to Ireland.'

At once Sean and the cart to which he had been tied rose swiftly into the air and, to the astonishment of the watching crowd, disappeared from sight.

Next morning Sean found himself and the cart resting at the front door of his cousin, Murty Farrell's house. Sean was still stunned and confused by his adventure, but very relieved to be safely back amongst friends again. Murty took a liking to the cart, which was the only reminder of his frightening experience and which naturally Sean had no great love for. A cheap bargain between the two men made Murty the proud owner of the fateful object.

On his return home, Sean found all the things in his cabin just as he had left them. Many a time afterwards he retold his story to friends and declared he would never forget the odd-looking Earl or the awe-inspiring judge that tried him. Above all he promised never again, as long as he lived, to interrupt the amusements of the fairies round his hearth.

The Captive Piper

A Fairy legend of Knockaney, Co. Limerick

RETOLD BY MARY McGARRY

Some people say that the Irish fairies have a peculiar language of their own which they always use in the presence of mortals whom they have abducted to the 'Otherworld'. It is very difficult to learn this fairy language, but once any human being gains an understanding of it, he is immediately expelled from the fairy realm, for the 'little people' jealously guard their secrets and the mysteries of their magic art.

Now long ago a certain renowned king of Munster, Ailill Olium, blemished his good reputation by cruelly mistreating the fair daughter of one of his defeated opponents. This princess, called Aine, soon followed her father to the grave and was buried on a prominent mound, named after her and now known as Knockaney.

Many centuries later, a local piper happened to be returning home from a wedding party in the early hours of a fine summer's morning. Donal O'Grady was his name and, since he was one of the best pipers in the province, his musical skill had been in such great demand that he had accompanied the dancing feet of the guests right through the preceding evening into the dawn of the new day. During the evening, in a few well earned respites from his music, Donal had enjoyed refreshments and the odd tumbler of punch, pressed on him by the happy host and hostess. Thus in high spirits he had played lively jigs, reels and hornpipes one after the other to the delight of the whole gathering. On parting all had wished him a good morning and safe home. And there he might have arrived in good time but, feeling slightly tired and weary as he passed the enchanted rath of Aine, he decided to take a short rest. Sitting on the green grass and breathing in the soft morning air, he took up his pipes and struck up a particularly joyful reel.

He had hardly begun to play when, glancing towards the rath, he saw a small door open on the embankment. Out rushed a number of tiny liveried men and, without more ado, they seized

Donal O'Grady and his pipes and whisked him within the opening, where he heard the door shut and bolt firmly behind him.

Wondering what was about to happen to him, Donal was hurried along the passage on the shoulders of the little men. Right at the end, another door flew open and there a most magnificent sight met his eyes. Hundreds of glowing lamps lit up a grand hall of vast proportions, spanned by an intricately decorated ceiling which was supported by monumental marble pillars. Assembled there was a fairy host of men and women attired in rich and colourful costumes. As he looked upwards to the top of the hall, on a throne of state Donal beheld a lady of great beauty. With a crown of gold that sparkled with diamonds resting on her long golden hair, she was holding court for the crowds of tiny figures that thronged to pay her homage. All about him were chattering gaily, but in a language he found impossible to comprehend. However, on hearing the name of Aine very frequently repeated, he guessed that it belonged to the fair queen who was the centre of all the activity before him.

For a long time Donal watched the fairy lords and ladies being presented to Queen Aine by a dapper little Master of Ceremonies – the men bowing very low, the women curtseying to the ground, and then both kissing the Queen's right hand before backing away with more bows and curtsies. Finally it was Donal's turn to be introduced and he was led forward to the steps at the foot of the throne. Not being very experienced in court etiquette, Donal was afraid he might not be able to imitate the graceful movements of his predecessors. So as humbly as possible he took off his old straw hat with his left hand, and tugging the front lock of hair on his forehead with the right, he gave a quick jerk with the right knee, bending the left. The fairy courtiers could not restrain their amusement, and chuckles were heard here and there. Donal was slightly hurt at what he felt was a great lack of manners, but forgot his pride when Aine smiled warmly at him and held out her hand for him to kiss. He was further reassured by what followed.

Donal was led to an elegant cushioned chair, where his pipes were placed on his knees ready for him to play. When the Queen gave her hand to some favoured courtier and all the other fairy lords began to select partners, Donal understood what was expected of him. While he set the pipes in motion, he noticed that the couples were ranged in two long lines and guessed that they wanted a sprightly country dance. He was puzzled for a few minutes to find the best and most suitable tune and settled at last on the 'Fairy Dance' which he thought would not be inappropriate on such an occasion.

A great deal of merriment and glee passed through the lines of fairies when he began to play. As the mazes of the dance were carried out by each successive couple, their piper regarded the appearance of his tiny dancers. All the fairy gentlemen he noticed, although well-dressed, were old and wizened looking. Amongst the ladies Aine stood out above all for her great beauty, and Donal swore he had never before seen any lady as fair as she.

The jigs, reels and country dances filled the vast hall until the fairy company had danced enough. At a signal from their Queen they filed past Donal with smiles of approval and graceful salutes. Then, in the twinkling of an eye they vanished, the lights were extinguished and the imprisoned piper was left alone in the darkness to reflect on the grandeur that had just passed away.

Donal turned his mind to escaping from the fairy world. But hard though he tried to find the passage through which he had entered, he could not make his way out at all. He spent several hours in this desolate state, until he became aware of fairies flitting through the hall above his head and jabbering to one another in their strange language he could not understand.

At last all the fairy men seemed to gather in a military array and mount on tiny steeds as if in preparation for an outdoor expedition. A dim ray of light began to outline their movements and he realised that the leader of the cavalcade was approaching the door at the entrance to the hall. Raising his sword the fairy leader shouted out, *'Tatther Rura'*, and the phrase was repeated right down the line of warriors. Instantly the door opened and all rushed out through the passage. The door banged shut behind them.

Donal realised he had learnt the fairies' password. Following in their wake he also cried out 'Tatther Rura'. The door opened as before and Donal made out the passage, which was clear of the cavalcade now bound on some distant journey. Hastening to the outer door, he again shouted the password, and as the door flew open he gazed once more on the green grass on the slopes of Knockaney.

For many a long day at fairs, christenings and weddings, where his lively music was much admired, he recounted his extraordinary presentation to Queen Aine.

Two Tales of Leprechauns

INTRODUCED BY MARY McGARRY

The leprechaun is the artisan of the fairy kingdom. He acts as tailor, shoe-maker, smith or coachbuilder to the elfin population. Often he is seen sitting, with a tiny hammer in his hand, hard at work on some new creation. He tends to be a solitary fairy, perhaps because he is of lower descent than his fellow fairies, his father being an evil spirit and his mother a degenerate fairy. By nature he is mischievous and fun-loving. The few people who have been lucky enough to catch a glimpse of him have described his appearance. He is quite small in size, rarely more than three feet tall. Usually he is dressed in a little green jacket and matching trousers, buckled at the knee, grey or black stockings and a tall, black hat cocked over his old, wrinkled face.

All the hidden treasures of the world are known to the leprechaun. For this reason the little fellow is constantly pursued by fortune-hunters but, being a wise and cunning sprite, he is normally able to out-smart them and seldom discloses his secrets. If you should come upon a leprechaun some evening in a lonely shrubbery, you must seize him firmly and keep your eyes fixed steadily on him, until he tells you all he knows. Should your glance stray, even for a moment, he will instantly be gone. Being very wily he will try every trick to distract your attention and free himself from your grasp and the fascination of your gaze. Yet, should you succeed in holding him, he can make you rich beyond your wildest dreams.

The following are two tales concerning the leprechaun and his 'crock of gold'.

The Magic Shilling

RETOLD BY MARY McGARRY

*a*ccording to tradition, the leprechaun owns a special purse containing a 'charmed shilling'. Though there is just a single shilling, no matter how often you draw out a coin from the purse it is never empty.

A young lad called Pat O'Reilly knew this tradition and looked long and hard for a leprechaun. He hated work above all else and hoped to become rich and carefree for the rest of his days.

One day on his way home, he spied a small green figure sitting on a piece of rock in the corner of a field. He crept up as quietly as possible and, grabbing the leprechaun by the collar, he pinned him to the ground.

'Well now, my little fellow, I have got you at last', he exclaimed proudly.

'You had better show me where the gold is, or for sure you will never see another day.' With that he shook the small body vigorously in the air.

The leprechaun begged to be released. He cried that he was not a real leprechaun and had no gold. But Pat was not going to be fooled by that and steadfastly refused to let him go. At last the leprechaun agreed to take him to a pot of gold hidden in a glen in Clare.

However, Pat was not very keen to travel such a long distance for fear that the slippery sprite might escape on the journey.

'Besides,' he said, 'I know full well there is gold hidden much nearer than that.'

'Would you let me go if I gave you a magic purse?' asked the leprechaun, hoping to persuade Pat with this reward. Pat thought he had better consent because he could not rely on being able to keep the rogue from escaping much longer. So he took the purse which was of the finest red silk, and looking inside he found a shining new shilling. While his attention was diverted the leprechaun vanished with a hideous laugh.

Pat, feeling very happy with his magic purse, made his way to a local tavern. There he met three acquaintances. In high spirits

30

he called the owner, Mrs. Moroney, and asked that they all be served with the very best drinks in the place.

'Where's your money?' she said suspiciously, for it was well known that Pat O'Reilly never had a penny to his name.

'No need to worry', he reassured her. 'I am a gentleman of fortune now, and you won't catch me doing an ounce of work again in this life. Come on, lads, drink at my expense!'.

So they did, and then Pat ordered a grand dinner for all. But Mrs. Moroney was still suspicious and said that nothing more would pass their lips until he had paid for what they already had.

'Alright, just as you wish,' said Pat, confidently taking out the magic purse. He recounted how he had come by it and his friends asked wonderingly, 'Was it really the leprechaun that gave it to you?'

'Indeed it was,' said Pat, 'and the virtue of this purse is that even if you take shillings out of it all the day long, they'll still be coming in a stream like whiskey out of a bottle.'

To prove it he pulled out a shilling. But, lo and behold, when he went to take out another one the purse was empty. The leprechaun had given him the wrong purse. A look of rage and embarrassment came over Pat's face when he saw what a fool the tiny imp had made of him. There he was with an enormous bill and just one shilling with which to pay it. Of course, no one believed his story now.

'Away with you and your leprechauns!' shouted Mrs. Moroney. 'You're just a liar and a thief.'

His companions were no less annoyed at being tricked, as they supposed, into drinking so much more than they could afford. To top it all, it looked as if they would have to pay Pat's share too. Angrily they took Pat by the shoulders and pushed him roughly round the room.

A passing constable, hearing the rumpus, came to find the cause of all the trouble.

'What's the harm in getting a purse from a leprechaun?' declared Pat, defending himself before the law.

'None at all,' said the policeman, 'if you can produce that leprechaun and make him testify that he gave it to you. Only that will prove you did not steal it.'

Of course poor Pat could not do this and he was put in jail. A sentence of thirty days hard labour was passed on him – the first he had ever done in his life. Needless to say, he was in no great hurry to meet a leprechaun again from that time on.

The Leprechaun of Carrigadhroid

RETOLD BY MARY McGARRY

On a steep rock rising out of the waters of the River Lee in County Cork stand the ruins of the very old Castle of Carrigadhroid. This story tells how the castle came to be built in such a wild and isolated region.

Once long ago on the edge of the Lee there lived a lonely widow and her poor son. The boy, called Donagh Caum O'Driscoll, tilled their small plot of land and tended their solitary cow on the banks of the river. From time to time he went fishing and brought his catch to sell in the market at Macroom, one of the most ancient towns in the kingdom.

Now, though Donagh was poor and crooked with a hump on his back, yet he was a warm-hearted and generous fellow. One day as he made his way to Macroom he stopped at the castle of the great Art Mor McCarthy. This chieftain was surnamed 'the Magnificent' because of the splendour in which he lived. But his extravagances had cost him so much that at this time he was penniless, and he could not provide for the needs of his household.

As Donagh approached, McCarthy and his beautiful daughter Maiga were standing at one of the windows. Cap in hand and willow basket on his arm, Donagh asked to see the chieftain's steward to try and sell him some of his fish. McCarthy expressed a wish to see the contents of Donagh's basket. Gladly Donagh displayed his wholesome collection of fish to the admiring eyes of the chief and his daughter. All the while Donagh was lost in contemplation of the lovely Maiga. The steward came forward to buy the fish, but realised he had no money to offer in return. Yet so enthralled was the fellow by the young lady of the castle, that he happily made a present of the fish to the chieftain.

Travelling home, Donagh could think of nothing but the fair Maiga with her long, flowing locks of raven-black hair and her dark eyes and graceful form. Her sweet voice echoed in his ears until his mother's shrill call brought him back to reality. But he could neither eat nor sleep and the widow became anxious for her only son for, deformed as he was, she loved him with all the sincere warmth and affection of a mother.

The next evening, as Donagh was wandering listlessly along the river bank, he strayed into a little wooded dell, that gently sloped down to the edge of the clear water. The shadows of evening were falling on the trees and bushes as the summer sun sank away on the horizon. Gazing at the pleasant scene, Donagh suddenly heard a slight tapping noise some distance away from him. The sound seemed to be coming from a clump of hazels, blackthorn and brier, out of the centre of which rose a tall, wide, spreading ash tree.

Creeping up very quietly, he saw a little figure not the height of half his leg, sitting on a tiny stool. The small fellow was hammering away at a minute shoe, which was laid across his knees. He seemed completely unaware of the human intruder. Donagh had often heard of the leprechauns and knew that it was one of their number that was there before him. Carefully he approached the fairy shoemaker.

'This is a fine evening for your work, my little man,' said Donagh, and fixed his eyes steadily on the leprechaun to prevent him from escaping.

'It is indeed, Donagh Caum,' replied the little man, looking a bit startled, but with a malicious grin.

'You're a fine little shoemaker,' said Donagh.

'Sure, I am nothing compared to that man standing behind you,' said the leprechaun.

But Donagh was well aware of the tricks these creatures use to free themselves from human power, so he refused to look away and replied, 'I would rather look at you yourself, my fine fellow.'

'Who's that coming over the river there?' said the leprechaun, pointing his finger in the direction of the water.

'You schemer!' said Donagh, picking up the leprechaun by his middle. 'Tell me where the money is or I'll kill you here and now.'

'Surely you would never murder a person as small and helpless as myself?' said the leprechaun, but the determined look on Donagh's face convinced him, and he agreed to tell his secrets. Donagh at that relaxed his hold on the tiny form.

'Do you know where the Giant's Causeway is?' said the leprechaun.

'I have heard talk of it', said Donagh.

'Well, then, at the foot of a big rock beneath a lone bush, right at the top of the cliff, there is a crock of gold that would buy the whole of Cork.'

'Oh, no!' said Donagh, 'You won't find me running from one end of the country to the other. You must tell me where there is gold hidden nearby, or else . . .'

'Please don't do that,' said the frightened leprechaun. 'Do you know where the hill of Tara is, then?'

'I have only heard talk of it' said Donagh.

'On the east side of the hill there is an old well where you can draw up a great treasure – gold, diamonds, silver – enough to buy the whole province of Munster,' said the little man.

'That's no good at all,' replied Donagh, 'I'll only release you when you tell me where I can easily find some gold.'

'All you do is talk,' said the leprechaun, looking around him in alarm, 'and there's Manus O'Mahony's mad bull charging straight towards us.'

'Where? where?' cried Donagh, who because he was lame could not run very fast, and looked fearfully in the direction pointed out by the little man. At that moment he heard a wild, unnatural laugh and the leprechaun vanished. Though bitterly disappointed Donagh consoled himself that he might come upon the leprechaun another time.

He returned home and told his mother about his adventure and how the leprechaun had finally beaten him. The old woman, wiser in this type of thing than her son, advised him, if he should ever have the chance again, to make the leprechaun give up his gold on the spot. She told him not to take any nonsense, but to press a sharp knife up against the creature's chest and demand the treasure.

In the meanwhile Donagh went fishing as usual and travelled to Macroom. Once more he visited the impoverished chieftain and was bewitched by the beauty of his daughter. Without a thought he gave away all his fish and, more deeply in love than ever, he left the castle.

His mother was surprised when her son arrived back in such a bewildered state and without the messages she had asked him to get in Macroom. But when questioned he answered so foolishly, that she decided he must have been fairy struck, and there was not much she could do to help him.

Carrigadhroid at this time was a wild, uninhabited spot; the craggy rock rose steeply from the river, and the banks were largely barren and rugged, with the exception of a few sheltered copses. It was this part of the river that Donagh liked best. From morning to eve he would lie stretched out on one of the small green patches on the rock face. Looking out over the water he would picture in his mind's eye the enchanting form of Maiga, and curse the lot of poverty and wretchedness that seemed to be his for life.

One evening while watching the setting sun he heard again the light tapping, which had led him before to the haunt of the leprechaun.

''Tis he again,' he said to himself, 'there's no one ever heard him once, or seen him once, who has not heard and seen him three times, if they don't obtain their wish at first. The third is the worst chance – now fortune befriend the poor cripple!'

Anxiously and cautiously he stole to the spot from which the noise was coming. There, seated at his old employment beneath an alder tree was the same withered old man as before. Donagh fixed his eyes steadily upon him and drawing a knife from his pocket, he rapidly approached the old man. As the tall shadow fell over him the little man looked up.

'It's you again, then, Donagh O'Driscoll, and how are you. Did you manage to get away from that mad bull the last time?' he chuckled.

'I have you again, you treacherous old miser' said Donagh, taking a firm hold of him, 'and you won't get away so easily this time.'

'Look at that fellow there', said the little fellow, 'making fun of your hump and crooked leg.'

'I'm not going to answer your questions this time,' said Donagh, 'but, as sure as I am standing here, if you don't bring up some gold this very minute, I'll kill you where you stand.'

'But listen to me, Donagh,' said the leprechaun, there is the beautiful Maiga and her father coming up along the riverside beyond.'

Donagh started, for this was the one tender point the little man could have touched upon. But luckily he refused to believe the trick and determined not to look round even if his life depended on it.

Again he ordered the leprechaun to bring up his gold if he wanted to save his life. He laid the leprechaun's back against a stone and put the point of his knife threateningly towards the tiny chest. 'I'll give you till I have counted to twenty,' he said, 'one, two, three . . .' By the time he had reached fifteen and got no response from the leprechaun, he pressed the knife angrily against the small body.

'Stop, Stop!' cried the leprechaun, 'you're a lucky man, Donagh O'Driscoll, for you have won the day. I'll give you what you ask, or more than you require.' Then he stamped with his foot upon the spot where he stood, which opened to reveal a long, deep earthen vessel filled to overflowing with gold and silver. A great many ancient and unusual ornaments, studded with diamonds and gems glittered in the fading light.

'But is this all real gold – will it not turn into nothing when you are gone,' said Donagh, hovering between joy and doubt at what had happened.

'Didn't I pledge my word,' said the leprechaun indignantly. Do you imagine I would break a promise once given. Now it is for you to let me go.'

With a violent jerk the leprechaun flung himself out of Donagh's grasp. In an instant he was transformed from the wrinkled old man into one young and fair-formed, though still tiny in size. 'Donagh,' he said, 'you will be happy – I have said it.' Then, breaking a branch from the alder tree, he struck Donagh a sharp blow across the face, which deprived him of his sight for a few minutes. When Donagh looked up again the leprechaun had disappeared.

The little cavern at his feet was still open, and there the treasure shone as brightly as before. Bending down, he gathered enough of the gold and silver to fill both his pockets. Carefully replacing the earthen vessel and covering it with clay and moss, he hastened home to show his mother his new-found fortune.

When she caught sight of her son, the old woman cried out in amazement 'Who are you at all? Your face and voice are those of my own boy, but he was humped and lame and you are straight and perfectly formed.' For Donagh had been so happy and excited about the gold that he had failed to notice the dramatic change in his appearance brought about by the power of the fairy man. Now he realised he had a double cause for rejoicing.

A rich and handsome man, he was able to buy all the lands belonging to the great chieftain, McCarthy, and woo his love, the Lady Maiga. She promised to marry him if he built a magnificent castle on the romantic rock of Carrigadhroid. This is how the fine castle was erected, and its lonely but beautiful ruins can be seen to this day.

The Phouka

BY LADY WILDE

*t*he Phouka is a friendly being, and often helps the farmer at his work if he is treated well and kindly. One day a farmer's son was minding cattle in the field when something rushed past him like the wind; but he was not frightened for he knew it was the Phouka on his way to the old mill by the moat where the fairies met every night.

So he called out, 'Phouka, Phouka, show me what you are like, and I'll give you my big coat to keep you warm.' Then a young bull came to him lashing his tail like mad; but Phadrig threw the coat over him, and in a moment he was quiet as a lamb, and told the boy to come to the mill that night when the moon was up, and he would have good luck.

So Phadrig went, but saw nothing except sacks of corn all lying about on the ground, for the men had fallen asleep, and no work was done. Then he lay down also and slept, for he was very tired: and when he woke up early in the morning there was all the meal ground, though certainly the men had not done it, for they still slept. And this happened for three nights, after which Phadrig determined to keep awake and watch.

Now there was an old chest in the mill, and he crept into this to hide, and just looked through the keyhole to see what would happen. And exactly at midnight six little fellows came in, each carrying a sack of corn upon his back; and after them came an old man in tattered rags of clothes, and he bade them turn the mill, and they turned till all was ground.

Then Phadrig ran to tell his father, and the miller determined to watch the next night with his son, and both together saw the same thing happen.

'Now,' said the farmer, 'I see it is the Phouka's work, and let him work if it pleases him, for the men are idle and lazy and only sleep. So I'll pack the whole set off tomorrow, and leave the grinding of the corn to this excellent old Phouka.'

After this the farmer grew so rich that there was no end to his money, for he had no men to pay, and all his corn was ground

without spending a penny. Of course the people wondered much over his riches, but he never told them about the Phouka or their curiosity would have spoiled the luck.

Now Phadrig went often to the mill and hid in the chest that he might watch the fairies at work; but he had great pity for the poor old Phouka in his tattered clothes, who yet directed everything and had hard work of it sometimes keeping the little Phoukas in order. So Phadrig, out of love and gratitude, bought a fine suit of cloth and silk and laid it one night on the floor of the mill just where the old Phouka always stood to give his orders to the little men, and then he crept into the chest to watch.

'How is this?' said the Phouka when he saw the clothes. 'Are these for me? I shall be turned into a fine gentleman.'

And he put them on, and then began to walk up and down admiring himself. But suddenly he remembered the corn and went to grind as usual, then stopped and cried out, 'No, no. No more work for me. Fine gentlemen don't grind corn. I'll go out and see a little of the world and show my fine clothes.' And he kicked away the old rags into a corner and went out.

No corn was ground that night, nor the next, nor the next; all the little Phoukas ran away, and not a sound was heard in the mill. Then Phadrig grew very sorry for the loss of his old friend, and used to go out into the fields and call out, 'Phouka, Phouka! come back to me. Let me see your face.' But the old Phouka never came back, and all his life long Phadrig never looked on the face of his friend again.

However, the farmer had made so much money that he wanted no more help; and he sold the mill, and reared up Phadrig to be a great scholar and a gentleman, who had his own house and land and servants. And in time he married a beautiful lady, so beautiful that the people said she must be daughter to the king of the fairies.

A strange thing happened at the wedding, for when they all stood up to drink the bride's health, Phadrig saw beside him a golden cup filled with wine. And no one knew how the golden cup had come to his hand; but Phadrig guessed it was the Phouka's gift, and he drank the wine without fear and made his bride drink also. And ever after their lives were happy and prosperous, and the golden cup was kept as a treasure in the family, and the descendants of Phadrig have it in their possession to this day.

Fair, Brown, and Trembling

BY JOSEPH JACOBS

K ing Hugh Curucha lived in Tir Conal, and he had three daughters, whose names were Fair, Brown, and Trembling.

Fair and Brown had new dresses, and went to church every Sunday. Trembling was kept at home to do the cooking and work. They would not let her go out of the house at all; for she was more beautiful than the other two, and they were in dread she might marry before themselves.

They carried on in this way for seven years. At the end of seven years the son of the king of Emania fell in love with the eldest sister.

One Sunday morning, after the other two had gone to church, the old henwife came into the kitchen to Trembling, and said, 'It's at church you ought to be this day, instead of working here at home.'

'How could I go?' said Trembling. 'I have no clothes good enough to wear at church; and if my sisters were to see me there, they'd kill me for going out of the house.'

'I'll give you,' said the henwife, 'a finer dress than either of them has ever seen. And now tell me what dress you will have?'

'I'll have,' said Trembling, 'a dress as white as snow, and green shoes for my feet.'

Then the henwife put on the cloak of darkness, clipped a piece from the old clothes the young woman had on, and asked for the whitest robes in the world and the most beautiful that could be found, and a pair of green shoes.

That moment she had the robe and the shoes, and she brought them to Trembling, who put them on.

When Trembling was dressed and ready, the henwife said, 'I have a honeybird here to sit on your right shoulder, and a honey-finger to put on your left. At the door stands a milk-white mare, with a golden saddle for you to sit on, and a golden bridle to hold in your hand.'

Trembling sat on the golden saddle, and when she was ready

to start, the henwife said, 'You must not go inside the door of the church, and the minute the people rise up at the end of Mass, do you make off, and ride home as fast as the mare will carry you.'

When Trembling came to the door of the church there was no one inside who could get a glimpse of her but was striving to know who she was; and when they saw her hurrying away at the end of Mass, they ran out to overtake her. But no use in their running, she was away before any man could come near her. From the minute she left the church till she got home, she overtook the wind before her, and outstripped the wind behind.

She came down at the door, went in, and found the henwife had dinner ready. She put off the white robes, and had on her old dress in a twinkling.

When the two sisters came home the henwife asked:

'Have you any news today from the church?'

'We have great news,' said they. 'We saw a wonderful grand lady at the church-door. The like of the robes she had we have never seen on woman before. It's little that was thought of our dresses beside what she had on; and there wasn't a man at the hurch, from the king to the beggar, but was trying to look at her and know who she was.'

The sisters would give no peace till they had two dresses like the robes of the strange lady, but honey-birds and honey-fingers were not to be found.

Next Sunday the two sisters went to church again, and left the youngest at home to cook the dinner.

After they had gone, the henwife came in and asked: 'Will you go to church today?'

'I would go,' said Trembling, 'if I could get the going.'

'What robe will you wear?' asked the henwife.

'The finest black satin that can be found, and red shoes for my feet.'

'What colour do you want the mare to be?'

'I want her to be so black and so glossy that I can see myself in her body.'

The henwife put on the cloak of darkness, and asked for the robes and the mare. That moment she had them. When Trembling was dressed, the henwife put the honey-bird on her right shoulder and the honey-finger on her left. The saddle on the mare was silver, and so was the bridle.

When Trembling sat in the saddle and was going away, the henwife ordered her strictly not to go inside the door of the church, but to rush away as soon as the people rose at the end of Mass, and hurry home on the mare before any man could stop her.

That Sunday the people were more astonished than ever, and gazed at her more than the first time; and all they were thinking of was to know who she was. But they had no chance, for the moment the people rose at the end of Mass she slipped from the church, was in the silver saddle, and home before a man could stop her or talk to her.

The henwife had the dinner ready. Trembling took off her satin robe, and had on her old clothes before her sisters got home.

'What news have you today?' asked the henwife of the sisters, when they came from the church.

'Oh, we saw the grand strange lady again! And it's little that any man could think of our dresses after looking at the robes of satin that she had on! And all at church, from high to low, had their mouths open, gazing at her, and no man was looking at us.'

The two sisters gave neither rest nor peace till they got dresses as nearly like the strange lady's robes as they could find. Of course they were not so good; for the like of those robes could not be found in Erin.

When the third Sunday came, Fair and Brown went to church dressed in black satin. They left Trembling at home to work in the kitchen, and told her to be sure and have dinner ready when they came back.

After they had gone and were out of sight, the henwife came to the kitchen and said, 'Well, my dear, are you for church today?'

'I would go if I had a new dress to wear.'

'I'll get you any dress you ask for. What dress would you like?' asked the henwife.

'A dress red as a rose from the waist down, and white as snow from the waist up; a cape of green on my shoulders; and a hat on my head with a red, a white, and a green feather in it; and shoes for my feet with the toes red, the middle white, and the backs and heels green.'

The henwife put on the cloak of darkness, wished for all these things, and had them. When Trembling was dressed, the henwife put the honey-bird on her right shoulder and the honey-finger on her left, and, placing the hat on her head, clipped a few hairs from one lock and a few from another with her scissors, and that moment the most beautiful golden hair was flowing down over the girl's shoulders. Then the henwife asked what kind of a mare she would ride. She said white, with blue and gold-coloured diamond-shaped spots all over her body, on her back a saddle of gold, and on her head a golden bridle.

The mare stood there before the door, and a bird sitting between her ears, which began to sing as soon as Trembling was in the saddle, and never stopped till she came home from the church.

The fame of the beautiful strange lady had gone out through the world, and all the princes and great men that were in it came to church that Sunday, each one hoping that it was himself would have her home with him after Mass.

The son of the King of Emania forgot all about the eldest sister, and remained outside the church, so as to catch the strange lady before she could hurry away.

The church was more crowded than ever before, and there were three times as many outside. There was such a throng before the church that Trembling could only come inside the gate.

As soon as the people were rising at the end of Mass, the lady slipped out through the gate, was in the golden saddle in an instant, and sweeping away ahead of the wind. But if she was, the Prince of Emania was at her side, and, seizing her by the foot, he ran with the mare for thirty perches, and never let go of the beautiful lady till the shoe was pulled from her foot, and he was left behind with it in his hand. She came home as fast as the mare could carry her, and was thinking all the time that the henwife would kill her for losing the shoe.

Seeing her so vexed and so changed in the face, the old woman asked, 'What's the trouble that's on you now?'

'Oh! I've lost one of the shoes off my feet,' said Trembling.

'Don't mind that; don't be vexed,' said the henwife; 'maybe it's the best thing that ever happened to you.'

Then Trembling gave up all the things she had to the henwife, put on her old clothes, and went to work in the kitchen. When the sisters came home, the henwife asked, 'Have you any news from the church?'

'We have indeed,' said they, 'for we saw the grandest sight to-day. The strange lady came again, in grander array than before. On herself and the horse she rode were the finest colours of the world, and between the ears of the horse was a bird which never stopped singing from the time she came till she went away. The lady herself is the most beautiful woman ever seen by man in Erin.'

After Trembling had disappeared from the church, the son of

46

the King of Emania said to the other kings' sons, 'I will have that lady for my own.'

They all said, 'You didn't win her just by taking the shoe off her foot; you'll have to win her by the point of the sword; you'll have to fight for her with us before you can call her your own.'

'Well,' said the son of the King of Emania, 'when I find the lady that shoe will fit, I'll fight for her, never fear, before I leave her to any of you.'

Then all the kings' sons were uneasy, and anxious to know who was she that lost the shoe; and they began to travel all over Erin to know could they find her. The Prince of Emania and all the others went in a great company together, and made the round of Erin; they went everywhere – north, south, east, and west. They visited every place where a woman was to be found, and left not a house in the kingdom they did not search, to know could they find the woman the shoe would fit, not caring whether she was rich or poor, of high or low degree.

The Prince of Emania always kept the shoe; and when the young women saw it, they had great hopes, for it was of proper size, neither large nor small, and it would beat any man to know of what material it was made. One thought it would fit her if she cut a little from her great toe; and another with too short a foot, put something in the tip of her stocking. But no use; they only spoiled their feet, and were curing them for months afterwards.

The two sisters, Fair and Brown, heard that the princes of the world were looking all over Erin for the woman that could wear the shoe, and every day they were talking of trying it on; and one day Trembling spoke up and said: 'Maybe it's my foot that the shoe will fit.'

'Oh, the breaking of the dog's foot on you! Why say so when you were at home every Sunday?'

They were that way waiting, and scolding the younger sister, till the princes were near the place. The day they were to come, the sisters put Trembling in a closet, and locked the door on her. When the company came to the house, the Prince of Emania gave the shoe to the sisters. But though they tried and tried, it would fit neither of them.

'Is there any other young woman in the house?' asked the prince.

'There is,' said Trembling, speaking up in the closet. 'I'm here.'

47

'Oh! we have her for nothing but to put out the ashes,' said the sisters.

But the prince and the others wouldn't leave the house till they had seen her; so the two sisters had to open the door. When Trembling came out, the shoe was given to her, and it fitted exactly.

The Prince of Emania looked at her and said, 'You are the woman the shoe fits, and you are the woman I took the shoe from.'

Then Trembling spoke up, and said, 'Do you stay here till I return.'

Then she went to the henwife's house. The old woman put on the cloak of darkness, got everything for her she had the first Sunday at church, and put her on the white mare in the same fashion. Then Trembling rode along the highway to the front of the house. All who saw her the first time said, 'This is the lady we saw at church.'

Then she went away a second time, and a second time came back on the black mare in the second dress which the henwife gave her. All who saw her the second Sunday said, 'That is the lady we saw at church.'

A third time she asked for a short absence, and soon came back on the third mare and in the third dress. All who saw her the third time said, 'That is the lady we saw at church.' Every man was satisfied, and knew that she was the woman.

Then all the princes and great men spoke up, and said to the son of the King of Emania, 'You'll have to fight now for her before we let her go with you.'

'I'm here before you, ready for combat,' answered the prince.

Then the son of the King of Lochlin stepped forth. The struggle began, and a terrible struggle it was. They fought for nine hours; and then the son of the King of Lochlin stopped, gave up his claim, and left the field. Next day the son of the King of Spain fought six hours, and yielded his claim. On the third day the son of the King of Nyerfoi fought eight hours, and stopped. The fourth day the son of the King of Greece fought six hours, and stopped. On the fifth day no more strange princes wanted to fight; and all the sons of kings in Erin said they would not fight with a man of their own land, that the strangers had had their chance, and, as no others came to claim the woman, she belonged of right to the son of the King of Emania.

The marriage-day was fixed, and the invitations were sent out.

The wedding lasted for a year and a day. When the wedding was over, the king's son brought home the bride, and when the time came a son was born. The young woman sent for her eldest sister, Fair, to be with her and care for her.

One day, when Trembling was well, and when her husband was away hunting, the two sisters went out to walk; and when they came to the seaside, the eldest pushed the youngest sister in. A great whale came and swallowed her.

The eldest sister came home alone, and the husband asked, 'Where is your sister?'

'She has gone home to her father in Ballyshannon; now that I am well, I don't need her.'

'Well,' said the husband, looking at her, 'I'm in dread it's my wife that has gone.'

'Oh! no,' said she. 'It's my sister Fair that's gone.'

Since the sisters were very much alike, the prince was in doubt. That night he put his sword between them, and said, 'If you are my wife, this sword will get warm; if not, it will stay cold.'

In the morning when he rose up, the sword was as cold as when he put it there.

It happened, when the two sisters were walking by the seashore, that a little cowboy was down by the water minding cattle, and saw Fair push Trembling into the sea; and next day, when the tide came in, he saw the whale swim up and throw her out on the sand.

When she was on the sand she said to the cowboy, 'When you go home in the evening with the cows, tell the master that my sister Fair pushed me into the sea yesterday; that a whale swallowed me, and then threw me out, but will come again and swallow me with the coming of the next tide; then he'll go out with the tide, and come again with to-morrow's tide, and throw me again on the strand. The whale will cast me out three times. I'm under the enchantment of this whale, and cannot leave the beach or escape myself. Unless my husband saves me before I'm swallowed the fourth time, I shall be lost. He must come and shoot the whale with a silver bullet when he turns on the broad of his back. Under the breast-fin of the whale is a reddish-brown spot. My husband must hit him in that spot, for it is the only place in which he can be killed.'

When the cowboy got home, the eldest sister gave him a draught of oblivion, and he did not tell.

Next day he went again to the sea. The whale came and cast Trembling on shore again. She asked the boy, 'Did you tell the

master what I told you to tell him?'

'I did not,' said he, 'I forgot.'

'How did you forget?' asked she.

'The woman of the house gave me a drink that made me forget.'

'Well, don't forget telling him this night; and if she gives you a drink, don't take it from her.'

As soon as the cowboy came home, the eldest sister offered him a drink. He refused to take it till he had delivered his message and told all to the master.

The third day the prince went down with his gun and a silver bullet in it. He was not long down when the whale came and threw Trembling upon the beach as the two days before. She had no power to speak to her husband till he had killed the whale. Then the whale went out, turned over once on the broad of his back, and showed the spot for a moment only. That moment the prince fired. He had but the one chance, and a short one at that; but he took it, and hit the spot, and the whale, mad with pain, made the sea all around red with blood, and died.

That minute Trembling was able to speak, and went home with her husband, who sent word to her father what the eldest sister had done. The father came, and told him any death he chose to give her to give it. The prince told the father he would leave her life and death with himself. The father had her put out then on the sea in a barrel, with provisions in it for seven years.

In time Trembling had a second child, a daughter. The prince and she sent the cowboy to school, and trained him up as one of their own children, and said: 'If the little girl that is born to us now lives, no other man in the world will get her but him.'

The cowboy and the prince's daughter lived on till they were married. The mother said to her husband, 'You could not have saved me from the whale but for the little cowboy: on that account I don't grudge him my daughter.'

The son of the King of Emania and Trembling had fourteen children, and they lived happily till the two died in old age.

The Well of D'yerree-in-Dowan

BY DOUGLAS HYDE

along time ago – before St. Patrick's time – there was an old king in Connacht, and he had three sons. The king had a sore foot for many years, and he could get no cure. One day he sent for the *Dall Glic** which he had, and said to him:

'I am giving you wages this twenty years, and you can't tell me what will cure my foot.'

'You never asked me that question before,' said the Dall Glic, 'but I tell you now that there is nothing in the world to cure you but a bottle of water from the Well of *D'yerree-in-Dowan*.'†

In the morning, the day on the morrow, the king called his three sons, and he said to them, 'My foot will never be better until I get a bottle of water from the Well of D'yerree-in-Dowan, and whichever of you will bring me that, he has my kingdom to get.'

'We will go in pursuit of it tomorrow,' says the three. The names of the three were Art, Nart (strength), and Cart (right).

On the morning of the day on the morrow, the king gave to each one of them a purse of gold, and they went on their way. When they came as far as the cross-roads, Art said, 'Each one of us ought to go a road for himself, and if one of us is back before a year and a day, let him wait till the other two come; or else let him set up a stone as a sign that he has come back safe.'

They parted from one another after that, and Art and Nart went to an inn and began drinking; but Cart went on by himself. He walked all that day without knowing where he was going. As the darkness of the night came on he was entering a great wood, and he was going forwards in the wood, until he came to a large house. He went in and looked round him, but he saw nobody, except a large white cat sitting beside the fire. When the cat saw him she rose up and went into another room. He was tired and sat

---

*Wise blind man.
†End of the World.

beside the fire. It was not long till the door of the chamber opened, and there came out an old hag.

'One hundred thousand welcomes before you, son of the king of Connacht,' says the hag.

'How did you know me?' says the king's son.

'Oh, many's the good day I spent in your father's castle in Bwee-sounee, and I know you since you were born,' said the hag.

Then she prepared him a fine supper, and gave it to him. When he had eaten and drunk enough, she said to him:

'You made a long journey to-day; come with me until I show you a bed. Then she brought him to a fine chamber, showed him a bed, and the king's son fell asleep. He did not awake until the sun was coming in on the windows the next morning.

Then he rose up, dressed himself, and was going out, when the hag asked him where he was going.

'I don't know,' said the king's son. 'I left home to find out the Well of D'yerre-in-Dowan.'

'I'm after walking a good many places,' said the hag, 'but I never heard talk of the Well of D'yerree-in-Dowan before.'

The king's son went out, and he was travelling till he came to a cross-roads between two woods. He did not know which road to take. He saw a seat under the trunk of a great tree. When he went up to it he found it written, 'This is the seat of travellers.'

The king's son sat down, and after a minute he saw the most lovely woman in the world coming towards him, and she dressed in red silk, and she said to him, 'I often heard that it is better to go forward than back.'

Then she went out of his sight as though the ground should swallow her.

The king's son rose up and went forward. He walked that day till the darkness of the night was coming on, and he did not know where to get lodgings. He saw a light in a wood, and he drew towards it. The light was in a little house. There was not as much as the end of a feather jutting up on the outside nor jutting down on the inside, but only one single feather that was keeping up the house. He knocked at the door, and an old hag opened it.

'God save all here,' says the king's son.

'A hundred welcomes before you, son of the king of the castle of Bwee-sounee,' said the hag.

'How do you know me?' said the king's son.

'It was my sister nursed you,' said the hag, 'and sit down till I get your supper ready.'

When he ate and drank his enough, she put him to sleep till morning. When he rose up in the morning, he prayed to God to direct him on the road of his luck.

'How far will you go to-day?' said the hag.

'I don't know,' said the king's son. 'I'm in search of the Well of D'yerree-in-Dowan.'

'I'm three hundred years here,' said the hag, 'and I never heard of such a place before; but I have a sister older than myself, and, perhaps, she may know of it. Here is a ball of silver for you, and when you will go out upon the road throw it up before you and follow it till you come to the house of my sister.'

When he went out on the road he threw down the ball, and he was following it until the sun was going under the shadow of the hills. Then he went into a wood, and came to the door of a little house. When he struck the door, a hag opened it and said, 'A hundred thousand welcomes before you, son of the king of the castle of Bwee-sounee, who were at my sister's house last night. You made a long journey to-day. Sit down; I have a supper ready for you.'

When the king's son ate and drank his enough, the hag put him to sleep, and he did not wake up till the morning. Then the hag asked, 'Where are you going?'

'I don't rightly know,' said the king's son. 'I left home to find out the Well of D'yerree-in-Dowan.'

'I am over five hundred years of age,' said the hag, 'and I never heard talk of that place before; but I have a brother, and if there is any such place in the world, he'll know of it. He is living seven hundred miles from here.'

'It's a long journey,' said the king's son.

'You'll be there to-night,' said the hag.

Then she gave him a little *garraun** about the size of a goat.

'That little beast won't be able to carry me,' said the king's son.

'Wait till you go riding on it,' said the hag.

The king's son got on the garraun, and out for ever with him as fast as lightning.

When the sun was going under, that evening, he came to a little house in a wood. The king's son got off the garraun, went in, and it was not long till an old grey man came out, and said, 'A hundred thousand welcomes to you, son of the king of the castle

---

*Nag, gelding.

of Bwee-sounee. You're in search of the Well of D'yerree-in-Dowan.'

'I am, indeed,' said the king's son.

'Many's the good man went that way before you; but not a man of them came back alive,' said the old man. 'However, I'll do my best for you. Stop here to-night, and we'll have sport to-morrow.'

Then he dressed a supper and gave it to the king's son, and when he ate and drank, the old man put him to sleep.

In the morning of the day on the morrow, the old man said, 'I found out where the Well of D'yerree-in-Dowan is; but it is difficult to go as far as it. We must find out if there's any good in you with the tight loop.'*

Then he brought the king's son out into the wood, gave him the loop, and put a mark on a tree two score yards from him, and told him to strike it. He drew the loop and struck the mark.

'You'll do the business,' said the old man.

They then went in, and spent the day telling stories till the darkness of the night was come.

When the darkness of the night was come, the old man gave him a loop and a sheaf of sharp stings† and said, 'Come with me now.'

They were going until they came to a great river. Then the old man said, 'Go on my back, and I'll swim across the river with you; but if you see a great bird coming, kill him, or we shall be lost.'

Then the king's son got on the old man's back, and the old man began swimming. When they were in the middle of the river the king's son saw a great eagle coming, and his gob (beak) open. The king's son drew the loop and wounded the eagle.

'Did you strike him?' said the old man.

'I struck him,' said the king's son, 'but here he comes again.'

He drew the loop the second time and the eagle fell dead.

When they came to the land, the old man said, 'We are on the island of the Well of D'yerree-in-Dowan. The queen is asleep, and she will not waken for a day and a year. She never goes to sleep but once in seven years. There is a lion and a monster (*uillphéist*) watching at the gate of the well, but they go to sleep at the same time with the queen, and you will have no difficulty in

---

*Bow
†Darts

going to the well. Here are two bottles for you; fill one of them for yourself, and the other for me, and it will make a young man of me.'

The king's son went off, and when he came as far as the castle he saw the lion and the monster sleeping on each side of the gate. Then he saw a great wheel throwing up water out of the well, and he went and filled the two bottles, and he was coming back when he saw a shining light in the castle. He looked in through the window and saw a great table. There was a loaf of bread, with a knife, a bottle, and a glass on it. He filled the glass, but he did not diminish the bottle. He observed that there was a writing on the bottle and on the loaf; and he read on the bottle, 'Water for the World,' and on the loaf, 'Bread For the World.' He cut a piece off the loaf, but it only grew bigger.

'My grief! That we haven't that loaf and that bottle at home,' said the king's son, 'and there'd be neither hunger nor thirst on the poor people.'

Then he went into a great chamber, and he saw the queen and eleven waiting-maidens asleep, and a sword of light hung above the head of the queen. It was it that was giving light to the whole castle.

When he saw the queen, he said to himself, 'It's a pity to leave that pretty mouth without kissing it. He kissed the queen, and she never awoke; and after that he did the same to the eleven maidens. Then he got the sword, the bottle, and the loaf, and came to the old man, but he never told him that he had those things.

'How did you get on?' said the old man.

'I got the thing I was in search of,' said the king's son.

'Did you see any marvel since you left me?' said the old man.

The king's son told him that he had seen a wonderful loaf, bottle, and sword.

'You did not touch them?' said the old man. 'Shun them, for they would bring trouble on you. Come on my back now till I bring you across the river.'

When they went to the house of the old man, he put water out of the bottle on himself, and made a young man of himself. Then he said to the king's son, 'My sisters and myself are now free from enchantment, and they are young women again.'

The king's son remained there until most part of the year and day were gone. Then he began the journey home; but, my grief, he had not the little nag with him. He walked the first day until the darkness of the night was coming on. He saw a large house. He went to the door, struck it, and the man of the house came out to him.

'Can you give me lodgings?' said he.

'I can,' said the man of the house, 'only I have no light to light you.'

'I have a light myself,' said the king's son.

He went in then, drew the sword, and gave a fine light to them all, and to everybody that was in the island. They then gave him a good supper, and he went to sleep. When he was going away in the morning, the man of the house asked him for the honour of God, to leave the sword with them.

'Since you asked for it in the honour of God, you must have it,' said the king's son.

He walked the second day till the darkness was coming. He went to another great house, beat the door, and it was not long till the woman of the house came to him, and he asked lodgings of her. The man of the house came and said:

'I can give you that; but I have not a drop of water to dress food for you.'

'I have plenty of water myself,' said the king's son.

He went in, drew out the bottle, and there was not a vessel in the house he did not fill, and still the bottle was full. Then a supper was dressed for him, and when he ate and drank his enough, he went to sleep. In the morning, when he was going, the woman asked of him, in the honour of God, to leave them the bottle.

'Since it has chanced that you ask it for the honour of God,' said the king's son, 'I cannot refuse you, for my mother put me under *gassa** before she died, never, if I could, to refuse anything that a person would ask of me for the honour of God.'

Then he left the bottle to them.

He walked the third day until darkness was coming, and he reached a great house on the side of the road. He struck the door; the man of the house came out, and he asked lodgings of him.

'I can give you that, and welcome,' said the man, 'but I'm grieved that I have not a morsel of bread for you.'

'I have plenty of bread myself,' said the king's son.

He went in, got a knife, and began cutting the loaf, until the table was filled with pieces of bread, and yet the loaf was a big as

---

*Mystic obligations

it was when he began. Then they prepared a supper for him, and when he ate his enough, he went to sleep. When he was departing in the morning, they asked of him, for the honour of God, to leave the loaf with them, and he left it with them.

The three things were now gone from him.

He walked the fourth day until he came to a great river, and he had no way to get across it. He went upon his knees, and asked God to send him help. After half a minute, he saw the beautiful woman he saw the day he left the house of the first hag. When she came near him, she said, 'Son of the king of the castle of Bwee-sounnee, has it succeeded with you?'

'I got the thing I went in search of,' said the king's son,' but I do not know how I shall pass over this river.'

She drew out a thimble and said: 'Bad is the day I would see your father's son without a boat.'

Then she threw the thimble into the river, and made a splendid boat of it.

'Get into that boat now,' said she, 'and when you will come to the other side, there will be a steed before you to bring you as far as the cross-road, where you left your brothers.'

The king's son stepped into the boat, and it was not long until he was at the other side, and there he found a white steed before him. He went riding on it, and it went off as swiftly as the wind. At about twelve o'clock on that day, he was at the cross-roads. The king's son looked round him, and he did not see his brothers, nor any stone set up, and he said to himself, 'perhaps they are at the inn.' He went there, and found Art and Nart, and they two-thirds drunk.

They asked him how he went on since he left them.

'I have found out the Well of D'yerree-in-Dowan, and I have the bottle of water,' said Cart.

Nart and Art were filled with jealousy, and they said one to the other, 'It's a great shame that the youngest son should have the kingdom.'

'We'll kill him, and bring the bottle of water to my father,' said Nart, 'and we'll say that it was ourselves who went to the Well of D'yerree-in-Dowan.'

'I'm not with you there,' said Art, 'but we'll set him drunk, and we'll take the bottle off him. My father will believe me and you before he'll believe our brother, because he has an idea that there's nothing in him but a half *omadawn*.'

'Then,' he said to Cart, 'since it has happened that we have come home safe and sound we'll have a drink before we go home.'

They called for a quart of whiskey, and they made Cart drink the most of it, and he fell drunk. Then they took the bottle of water from him, went home themselves, and gave it to the king. He put a drop of the water on his foot, and it made him as well as ever he was.

Then they told him that they had great trouble to get the bottle of water – that they had to fight giants, and to go through great dangers.

'Did ye see Cart on your road?' said the king.

'He never went farther than the inn, since he left us,' said they, 'and he's in it now, blind drunk.'

'There never was any good in him,' said the king, 'but I cannot leave him there.'

Then he sent six men to the inn, and they carried Cart home. When he came to himself, the king made him into a servant to do all the dirty jobs about the castle.

When a year and a day had gone by, the queen of the Well of D'yerree-in-Dowan and her waiting-maidens woke up and the queen found a young son by her side, and the eleven maidens the same.

There was great anger on the queen, and she sent for the lion and the monster, and asked them what was become of the eagle that she left in charge of the castle.

'He must be dead, or he'd be here now, when you woke up,' said they.

'I'm destroyed, myself, and the waiting-maidens ruined,' said the queen, 'and I never will stop till I find out the father of my son.'

Then she got ready her enchanted coach, and two fawns under it. She was going till she came to the first house where the king's son got lodging, and she asked was there any stranger there lately. The man of the house said there was.

'Yes! said the queen, 'and he left the sword of light behind him; it is mine, and if you do not give it to me quickly I will throw your house upside down.'

They gave her the sword, and she went on till she came to the second house, in which he had got lodging, and she asked was there any stranger there lately. They said that there was. 'Yes,' said she, 'and he left a bottle after him. Give it to me quickly, or I'll throw the house on ye.'

They gave her the bottle, and she went till she came to the third house, and she asked was there any stranger there lately. They said there was.

'Yes!' said she, 'and he left the loaf of lasting bread after him. That belongs to me, and if ye don't give it to me quickly I will kill ye all.'

She got the loaf, and she was going, and never stopped till she came to the castle of Bwee-Sounee. She pulled the *cooalya-coric** and the king came out.

'Have you any son?' said the queen.

'I have,' said the king.

'Send him out here till I see him.' said she.

The king sent out Art, and she asked him, 'Were you at the Well of D'yerree-an-Dowan?'

'I was,' said Art.

'And are you the father of my son?' said she.

'I believe I am,' said Art.

'I will know that soon,' said she.

Then she drew two hairs out of her head, flung them against the wall, and they were made into a ladder that went up to the top of the castle. Then she said to Art, 'If you were at the Well of D'yerree-in-Dowan, you can go up to the top of that ladder.'

Art went up half way, then he fell, and his thigh was broken.

'You were never at the Well of D'yerree-in-Dowan,' said the queen.

Then she asked the king, 'Have you any other son?'

'I have,' said the king.

'Bring him out,' said the queen.

Nart came out, and she asked him, 'Were you ever at the Well of D'yerree-in-Dowan?'

'I was,' said Nart.

'If you were, go up to the top of that ladder,' said the queen.

He began going up, but he had not gone far till he fell and broke his foot.

'You were not at the Well of D'yerree-in-Dowan,' said the queen.

Then she asked the king if he had any other son, and the king said he had. 'But,' said he, 'it's a half fool he is, that never left home.'

'Bring him here,' said the queen.

---

*Pole of combat

When Cart came, she asked him, 'Were you at the Well of D'yerree-in-Dowan?'

'I was,' said Cart, 'and I saw you there.'

'Go up to the top of that ladder,' said the queen.

Cart went up like a cat, and when he came down she said, 'You are the man who was at the Well of D'yerree-in-Dowan, and you are the father of my son.'

Then Cart told of the trick his brothers played on him, and the queen was going to slay them, until Cart asked pardon for them. Then the king said that Cart must get the kingdom.

Then the father dressed him out and put a chain of gold beneath his neck, and he got into the coach along with the queen, and they departed to the Well of D'yerree-in-Dowan.

The waiting-maidens gave a great welcome to the king's son, and they all of them came to him, each one asking him to marry herself.

He remained there for one-and-twenty years, until the queen died, and then he brought back with him his twelve sons, and it is from them that the twelve tribes of Galway are descended.

Country-Under-Wave

BY ALICE FURLONG

*t*here was once a little child, and he could not learn. It was not his fault. Every summer eve, and every winter night, he stood by the knee of his mother, and she said for him the names of the days of the week, and the seasons of the year, and told him how to call the sun and the moon and the stars. She gave him to know that the wheat was sown in one time, and reaped in another; that the oxen drew the plough, and the swift, nimble steed the chariot; that there were seven degrees of folks in the land, and seven orders among the poets, and seven colours to be distributed among the folks and among the poets, according to rank and station. And many other things the mother taught him, standing by her knee. The child listened, and was of attentive mind.

But in the morning, she asked him what was shining in the heavens, and he made answer, 'The moon.' And she asked him when did men take sickles and go a-reaping, and he said, 'In the season of Beltaine' (which is the early summer season when birds are on the bough, and blossom on the thorn). And she bade him tell her what animal it was that drew the plough over red, loamy fields, and he answered, 'The swift, nimble horse.' And she questioned him of the seven folks, and the seven orders, and the seven colours, and he had no right understanding concerning any of these.

'Ill-luck is on me, that I am the mother of a fool!' said the poor woman many a time. Then the child used to steal away to the dim, green orchard, and hide among the mossy trees, and weep.

After a time, the mother gave up trying to teach him, and taught his younger brothers and his sister, instead. The boy then took the lowest place at table, and his fare was given him last, and he was, in that homestead, the person held in least respect by menservants and maids.

There was a wise woman tarrying in the place a day, putting herbs of healing about an ailing cow. She saw the boy, and his fair head hanging, and shame in his eyes. 'What is wrong with this fair-headed lad?' said she.

'The head is wrong with him,' answered the mother of the boy. 'He has no utterance nor understanding. A heavy trouble to me, that! For there was none among my kin and people but had the wisdom and the knowledge fitting for his station.'

The wise woman muttered and mumbled to herself.

'Get him the Nuts of Knowledge', said she, after that.

'I have heard tell of them,' said the mother, 'but hard is their getting.' The brothers and the sister of the child that could not learn stood round about, and listened to the talk between the mother and the wise woman, Dechtera.

'The Nuts of Knowledge, they grow upon the Hazels of Knowledge, over a Well of Enchantment in the Country-under-Wave,' said Dechtera. 'If it be that you desire wisdom for your boy, good woman, you must send there some person to bring the nuts to you.'

The second son, Kian, flung back his hair. He was a proud youth, and full of courage as a ripe apple is full of sweetness.

'Let me be going, that the disgrace may be taken from my mother, and the sons of my mother,' said he.

The wise woman fingered her long lip.

'If you would go, 'tis soon you must be going,' she said. 'It is near the Eve of Beltaine, an eve of great witchery. Between the rising and the setting of the moon, that night, the loughs and the seas of Erinn become gates of glass that will open to let through any person who seeks the Country-under-Wave. Is this to your mind, my son?'

'It is pleasing to my mind,' said the lad.

'It is well pleasing to my mind,' said the mother.

The wise woman went on telling them of the way to reach Country-under-Wave.

'He must bid farewell to kith and kin, and go in his loneness to the lough-shore that night,' she said. 'And when the gates of glass are shut behind him, he must tarry in the Under-water Land from Beltaine until Samhain and harvest, when the nuts of the Magic Hazels will ripen to scarlet red. And on the eve of Samhain, he will draw near the Well of Enchantment and wait for the dropping of the nuts. He must be swift to stretch the hand and snatch them as they drop. For the Salmon of Knowledge, he is waiting in the Well, to eat the fruit as it falls. In that hour, a rosy surge rises upon the water, and the Salmon eats and swims away, swimming all the seas of the round, rolling world. And he has a knowledge of everything that passes, over-seas, and under-seas, and in hidden places and desert ways. But if this youth let the nuts slip through his fingers, he shall be in the power of Them in the Country-under-Wave.'

'Good are my fingers to catch and hold,' said the boy, Kian.

The wise woman went away to the hills then, after curing the ailing cow.

Came the eve of Beltaine, the night of witchery. The lad said farewell to his house and home, and embraced his brothers and his sister and his mother. He went out alone under the moon, and there was fairy singing in the wind that night, and over the dewy fields the silver track of fairy feet. He came to the lough shore, and saw the water as gates of glass. He went boldly through and travelled crystal roadways and riverways until he came to the Country-under-Wave.

The grass was greener than emeralds there; the trees were bowers of blossom. A radiant mist was on the mountains. The level plain was more thick with flowers than the sky with stars of a night when there is neither moon nor cloud. 'A better country than my mother's country!' said the youth to himself.

He was walking over a shining pebbly way until he came to a house. Every plank of the wall was of a different colour to the one beside it; the doors and windows were framed and pillared in wrought gold; the roof was fashioned of plumage so finely spread that it seemed like one feather witout parting or division.

People were passing to and fro about this fair house. Noble of mien were they, with hair of the hue of primroses, with eyes sloe-black, the blush of the rosy foxglove on every cheek, the pure whiteness of milk on every brow. They came in a shining troop to meet Kian, the boy, and they said to him, 'A hundred welcomes before you!'

The lad saluted them. They brought him within the palace, and invited him to abide there for the night. He said he was willing. The time went pleasantly with mirth and music. Soon the lad inquired where was the Well of Enchantment? 'More than a day's journey from this spot,' the lord of the mansion made answer. On the red dawn of the morrow, the lad took his leave of them. They gave him a fair-woven napkin spun of silk as fine as the web of a spider.

'When there comes upon you hunger or thirst, spread thst napkin on the grass and it shall be covered with the choicest of foods and drinks,' said the lord of the coloured house.

The lad gave them thanks.

'It is a great country you have of it down here,' he said. The noble people were pleased.

'You never were in its like before,' they said.

The boy, Kian, felt his high spirit rise up in him. He was a proud lad, and could not listen to a country being praised over his own. That was no fault. But he spoke a word, and the word was not true.

'As many wonders have I seen in my mother's country, and more,' said he. Then he followed the crystal waterways and roadways, seeking the Well of Enchantment.

The folks of that mansion were watching him along the way. 'A lie in his mouth in return for our hospitality!' said they one to another. 'Well, let it be so. He is not in our power now, but that may be mended another day.'

The boy followed his road. He was travelling till evening, and he came to the shore of the sea. The sand was in grains of gold, the waves fell with the sound of singing. He beheld white-maned seahorses race upon the strand, and wonderful people in chariots behind the horses. He sat down among the flowers, and he spread the fine-spun napkin, and it was covered with choice food and drinks. He ate his supper, and then looked about to find a place to rest for the night.

He saw a fair woman coming towards him, and gave her greeting.

'A hundred welcomes before you, Kian,' said she to him. He wondered how she knew his name. 'You are in want of a resting-place for the night?' said she.

'I want that, among other things,' said the lad.

The fair woman led him to a palace among the rocks. It was finer and better than the first house he had been in, if that were possible. Every person there had a star on the forehead and flowing pale-gold hair, like the ripple of the foam of the sea. And the clothing of every person was of the tint of waves, blue and green, shifting and changing with their stir and movement.

'This is the house of Manannan Mac Lir, who puts command upon the winds and the storms and the tempests that wreck ships and drown fishers,' said the woman.

The boy remained there that night. Pleasant was the entertainment he got in the house of Manannan Mac Lir. On the morn of the morrow, he went forth again to find the Well of Enchantment. The folks of the house gave him a little bit of a cloak, no bigger than would go over the lad's shoulders.

'When you are in want of a shelter and sleeping booth for the night, hang this cloak from the first straight twig you pick up from the grass. The twig will be a pillar and the cloak a tent, therewith.'

He gave them thanks, and said, 'Wonders upon wonders! What more can you do down here?'

The sea-folks laughed out. They laughed more softly than the sigh of summer waves. They were pleased with the youth.

'You have not fallen in with such people before,' said they. The spirit of the lad rose up. He forgot himself again. He told another lie.

'The foot-boys of the King of Erinn are better people,' he said, and followed his journey. The folks of that sea-mansion laughed again. But now their laughter was like the whistle of the wind that bids the storm begin.

'A boast he has instead of thanks for us,' said they. 'Let it remain so. He is not in our power now. That will be mended another day.'

Kian, the boy, abode in the Country-under-Wave while the meadows ripened in his mother's country, and mowers went forth with scythes, and maids tossed the hay. The apple was green and the cherry was red. After that, it drew nigh the harvest, and the apple reddened, and the cherry tree began to change the hue of its leaves.

Down in the Country-under-Wave, the youth was walking to and fro, seeking the Well of Enchantment. The day before the eve of Samhain, he came upon it, in a deep forest, where the wind murmured always and always. He saw the magic hazels, and knew them by the crimson of their fruit. And the nut-cluster drooped over the water of the Well, and leaned to its own rosy shadow beneath. 'Now my journey is ended,' said Kian, the boy.

He hung his cloak from the first twig he met in the green, green grass, and it rose to be a pillar, and the cloak spread to be a tent. He threw his fine-spun napkin upon the flowers, and it was covered with food and drinks. He ate his supper, and he took his rest.

But the people of the first mansion had put a sleeping potion in the drink, and it was long that Kian remained in slumber. All the morning he slept; and the noonday sun saw him sleeping, and the rising moon that night. But just before the midnight he awoke, for he seemed to hear his young sister calling upon him to haste, haste, haste. He ran out in the moonlight, and saw the Well shining, and the magic cluster swaying from the bough.

'It is my time now,' said he.

He stood beside the water, and there was the shimmering salmon, with upturned eye, below. But while he waited, all of a sudden, from the tent behind him came the most woeful crying he had ever heard. He thought it was the voice of his mother, and he turned his head. And then, he heard a splash in the water of the Well of Enchantment. The crying ceased as sudden as it began. It was a high, wild cry of laughter he caught, like the wind at night when tempest is out. And the waters of the Well began to rise in a rosy surge, and there was no cluster hanging to its own shadow, but a fruitless bough.

'Now, ill-luck is upon me!' said Kian, the boy.

The water sank, and the Salmon of Knowledge swam to the seas of the round, rolling world. The boy sat down by the brink, and covered his head with his mantle, lest any eye might discern his tears. And as he was thus, a deep sleep fell upon him, like to death itself. Then the people of the coloured mansion, and the sea-folks of the palace of Manannan came round him, and they put a grey flagstone over him, and left him by the Well.

November eve came and went, and the mother of Kian was looking for his return, but he never came. 'I had a bad dream concerning him,' said the little sister, Fedelm.

The mother sent for the wise woman on the hill.

'Some mishap has befallen,' said Dechtera. 'I do not know what you had best do now, except you send the third brother to help him. But you must wait for next May-eve.'

The woman of the house made lament and moan. 'For a fool has this trouble fallen,' said she. She drove the eldest boy from her presence, and made him sit with the servants. But little Fedelm wept until, for peace sake, the mother had to let him back to his own place. The poor boy that could not learn was filled with shame.

In due season, came the time of Beltaine, the eve of witchery. Lugaid, the third of the brothers, went forth, in his loneness. He heard the fairy talk in the wind, and saw, among the dew, the silver track of the feet of Queens from the Raths. He stepped upon the lough shore, and the gates of glass stood open, and he went through. Not gleefully he went, but against his will, for he cared for no person in the world but himself – neither for the shame of the fool, nor for the lost, bright boy, nor for the sorrow of his mother. But he said to himself, 'Bad is it that I must go upon this search. But worse it will be if I stay at home, for our house is full of weeping and misery, and there is no comfort to be had in it.'

He was walking crystal streets and roads until he came to the Country-under-Wave, in like manner to his brother. He beheld the bowers and the flowers, the mist of light upon the mountains. He saw the coloured house, and the noble people in their beauty.

They came to him. 'A hundred welcomes before you!' said they. He was too fond of his own comfort to doff his head-dress to them.

'In a strange country, no stranger goes without supper,' he said.

The people whispered among themselves. They said then, 'If you had not asked it, it would have been given to you.' They brought him within the palace, and gave him his supper, full and plenty of all kinds. They kept him there that night.

When morning was come, and the crowing of cocks, and a red sun rising, he said to them, 'Is it far to the Well of Enchantment?'

'It will take you nigh a season to find it,' said they to him. He sighed at that, and the lord of the mansion took pity upon him. He gave him a fine-spun napkin, and told him it would be spread with breakfast, dinner, and supper for him, as long as he remained in that place. The lad bade them joy, and went off whistling. He did not doff his head-dress to the women, and he going.

The noble people were angry. 'A churl this is, no lie,' they said. 'Well, he is not in our power to-day, but that will be mended another day.'

Lugaid went up and down that country. He came to the shore, and the ribbed, yellow sands, and the waves that made music in their plash and fall. The steeds of Manannan Mac Lir raced upon the sea. His chariots glistened; his people were there, in glinting, sheeny garments, all changing from green to blue, and from blue to green again.

It was night-fall when the lad beheld them, and no light was abroad but the light from the star on the brow of every one of these strange sea-people. One of them came to him. 'You will be in want of shelter to-night?' she said. The boy had been sleeping in dry places under hedges and southern banks. He felt he would like better the comfort of a bed.

'Shelter is a good thing to a tired person, and the night to be at hand,' he answered. She brought him with her into the palace among the rocks. He sat on a couch made of the down of sea swans; he drank out of a cup that was speckled with great emeralds as the grass of a May morning with beads of dew.

There was reciting of hero-tales, and harping and piping, after the banquet. The lad, Lugaid, was heavy with sleep. He let his head fall down, and snored.

'O, 'tis a churl we have in it!' cried the people of Manannan. 'Throw him out with the calves in the byre!'

The fair woman who had spoken first with the boy, took his part. 'Long travel he has put over him,' said she, 'and in the shelter of a house he has not slept for nights upon nights.' They let him be, then, until it was morning.

When the morn of the morrow came, the sea-folks gave him the little cloak. 'A tent it will be for you when you need it,' said they.

It was a little grey thing, mean to look at. The lad did not believe in the power of the sea-people. He took the cloak and threw it upon his back, and went away, swaggering, and making faces at them over his shoulder. But as he went, he heard them all begin to talk together, and their voices were like the rising of the far tide. 'It is not in our power to harm him, now,' they were saying, 'but that will be amended another day.'

The young lad abode in that Country-under-Wave until Samhain. Everywhere he went, he kept his eyes open for a sight of his brother. But he asked no questions of anybody. In due time he found the deep forest, and the dark Well, the hazels and the ruddy fruit, leaning to its own shadow.

It was sunset on the eve of Samhain. The boy sat down on the ground, near an old grey flag-stone. He spread the napkin out, and there was an abundance both of food and drink upon it, at that. He ate and drank.

But the people of the coloured house had put a sleeping potion into the drink, for on this eve they had power to work spells and charms against mortals. The boy drank then, and a heavy slumber fell upon him, and he was there lying in the dew until midnight drew nigh.

He heard in his sleep the voice of his sister, Fedelm. 'O, haste, haste, haste!' said the voice. He rose and ran to the Well of Enchantment. The rosy cluster was loosening from the bough. Lugaid, the boy, stretched his hand, and his eye caught the silver gleam of the Salmon of Knowledge below in the water of the Well. But a gust of hollow wind sprang up, all at once, and blew the leaves of the magic hazels into his eyes. Then he heard the fall of the fruit upon the water, and the crimson surge swelled up with little dim noises, and the Salmon ate the nuts, and swam away to the seas of the round, rolling world.

The deep death-trance fell upon Lugaid. He dropped down beside the Well. The sea-folks, and the people of the coloured mansion came, and put a grey flag-stone over him and left him by his brother.

The mother waited for her boy's return, but he did not return.

'I saw him in my dream,' said Fedelm, the girl. 'I saw him, and he was in a trance of sleep.'

The mother sent for Dechtera, the wise woman.

'Lugaid has gone the way of Kian,' said the poor mother. 'What will I be doing now, with no son left me but a fool?'

'Send the daughter after them,' said Dechtera.

'I will not send the daughter,' said the woman of the house. She kissed and embraced the child, and said that she would not part with her. The boy that could not learn said he would not part with her. The mother blessed him for that, and put him into his own proper place at the head of his father's table. There was peace and sorrow among them until it was May-eve again.

'I will go to my rest early tonight,' said Fedelm, the girl.

They did not know what she had in her mind to do. They let her away to her little bower, to her rest. But she wound a silken curtain about the bedpost, and let herself down through the window. She went over the bawn in the light of the moon, and heard the fairy-women singing in the wind, and saw the glimmer of fairy feet dancing over the honey-dew.

She went in her loneness to the lough shore, and the gates of glass stood open. She took a quick breath, and leaped through, and travelled the crystal highways and glassy roads until she came to the Country-under-Wave.

She found the lovely meads, thick-set with blossoms and the embowering trees. She saw the mountain mist, like silver fleeces spread far and thin. She fared to the coloured mansion with its golden pillars, and met the wise people of that house.

'A hundred welcomes before you, fair maid!' said they to her.

'A hundred tears are falling after me,' said Fedelm.

They brought her within, and laid choice foods before her. She ate a little honey and bread, and no more. She asked them to tell her the road to the Well of Enchantment.

'It is more than a month's journey from here,' said they.

71

She rose up then, and said she must be on her way though the night was falling. But they besought her, and craved of her to remain in their company that night, since there was now naught to be seen by the Well but hazels with rosy buds upon them. She waited, then, that night.

In the morning they said to her, 'Here is a napkin. Whenever you are hungry or thirsty spread it on the ground, and it shall hold its full of food and drink.'

Fedelm took it, and made them a curtsy. 'Is there anything I may do for ye, in return for this gift,' said she.

'Teach a boy to speak truth,' said the lord of the mansion. 'You will not see us again.'

The girl went her way. She fared north and south. She fared east and west. She came to the green-billowed, foam-ridged, hollow sea. The waves were making a melodious, wandering music. The seahorses pawed the floor of the ocean, and tossed the surf of the high, towering tide.

Manannan and his people were in their chariots, racing and riding on the watery meads. Little Fedelm stood watching them, and the evening fell, and she was so entranced that she forgot to eat or drink.

Then a fair radiant woman came to her, over the seas. She was more lustrous than the evening star when it hangs over the new moon in a twilight blue sky.

'I saw a face like this before,' said she. 'And I saw such clear bright eyes. Who will this little mortal maiden be?' And she stood before Fedelm, and looked her up and down.

'A maiden on a sad quest,' said the girl. 'The dauther of a sad mother; the sister of a sad brother.' Her tears fell, and left her eyes more clear and bright again. The majestic women brought her into the sea palace. They made her remain with them for that night. There was music and singing, and they asked her if the same was pleasing. She answered, 'If one were in mournful mood that harping and those singing voices would be enough to make him forget his sadness, though it were the whole world's burden should be upon him.'

'A well-spoken maiden,' said the sea-folks among themselves.

On the morn of the morrow, they gave her the small grey cloak, and knowledge of the use of it.

'What shall I do to repay you for this gift?' said Fedelm, curtsying before them.

'Teach a churl fine manners,' said the sea-folks. 'This is our first and last meeting.'

The girl was in the Country-under-Wave until November eve. She found the dim ever-murmuring wood, and the dark deep Well of Enchantment, and the Magic Hazels. The cluster was scarlet-red, swaying above its shadow in the water. The two grey flag-stones were beside. The girl looked at the first of them. It had a streak of moss down the middle of the top.

'That puts me in mind of the curl on the white forehead of Kian, my brother,' said the maid. 'But it was hair brighter than gold, and this is the old green moss on the old grey flag-stone.'

She went wandering about the lone place, and stood by the second flag-stone. There was a score down the middle of the top.

'That, moreover, puts me in mind of my brother, Lugaid, and the frown he used to have on his brow, a furrow of discontent,' said she, musing. 'But what is this but an old grey stone, and he had a brow fairer than snow.'

After that, the evening fell, and all the murmuring, whispering wind of the woods went into a strange silence. And soon the moon rose, round as an apple, and the stars came out, twinkling and beaming over the dew.

Fedelm ate her supper off the magic napkin, and rested a while beneath the enchanted cloak. She was weary. A sleep fell upon her. But in the slumber she seemed to hear faint voices crying and calling. It went to her heart to hear them, for she knew them as the voices of her two lost brothers. She came to herself at the sound. It was the people of the coloured house made her hear the voices. She walked out upon the brink of the Well of Enchantment.

'I discern a creaking in that bough,' she said. If it had not been that the forest was full of silence, she would not have heard it; but this was the work of the sea-folks, to lay a spell of silence on the leaves, that the girl might know the hour was at hand.

It drew near the midnight, and Fedelm stood upon the brink of the Well, and watched the swaying of the bough, and the magic cluster, crimson-red. She saw below her in the wave a great silver salmon, waiting, with upturned eye. And then, the bough creaked, the stalk snapped, and the nuts, shining like fiery rubies, came dropping down upon the water. But the magic cluster never reached the wave, for Fedelm's little fingers seized it as it fell.

The moment the nuts were in her hand she knew all things.

73

She knew the flag-stone with the streak of moss upon it was her dear brother, Kian, who had told a lie to the people of the coloured mansion. She knew the flag-stone with the furrow was Lugaid, the churlish, selfish brother. And she knew how to break the spell upon the one and the other by shaking the water of the Well of Enchantment over them from her little kind hand.

She did that, and they came into their right shapes, and embraced her, and laughed and cried. She led them out by the crystal waterways and roadways, and the gates of glass. They all went back to their mother's house, and great was the welcome they got there.

And the boy that could not learn, he ate the Nuts of Knowledge. From that day, he knew all things, the talking of the wind and the whisper of the reeds and rushes, the call of birds, and the cry of beasts, and there was nothing in the whole wide world hidden from him after that day.

The Enchanted Island

ANON

To Rathlin's Isle I chanced to sail
　When summer breezes softly blew,
And there I heard so sweet a tale,
　That oft I wished it could be true.
They said, at eve, when rude winds sleep,
　And hushed is ev'ry turbid swell,
A mermaid rises from the deep,
　And sweetly tunes her magic shell.

And while she plays, rock dell and cave
　In dying falls the sound retain,
As if some choral spirits gave
　Their aid to swell her witching strain.
Then summoned by that dulcet note,
　Uprising to th' admiring view,
A fairy island seems to float
　With tints of many a gorgeous hue.

And glittering fanes, and lofty towers,
　All on this fairy isle are seen;
And waving trees, and shady bowers,
　With more than mortal verdure green.
And as it moves, the western sky
　Glows with a thousand varying rays;
And the calm sea, tinged with each dye,
　Seems like a golden flood of blaze.

They also say, if earth or stone,
　From verdant Erin's hallowed land,
Were on this magic island thrown,
　For ever fixed, it then would stand,
But, when for this, some little boat
　In silence ventures from the shore –
The mermaid sinks – hushed is the note,
　The fairy isle is seen no more!

76

The Fairy Tree

RETOLD BY MARY McGARRY

Long ago on the green plain beside the lakes of Lein of the Crooked Teeth, now known as the Lakes of Killarney, the fairy race of the Dedannans played a game of hurley against the Fianna. For three days and three nights they continued to play, but neither side could score a single goal. When they realised that they could not overcome the men of the plains, the fairy people returned to their kingdom in the North.

For their food during the game and on the journey the fairies had brought along with them from fairyland tiny bags filled with various delicacies. They dined on fruits far superior to any that grow in this world, but their favourite fruit by far was the red quicken berry. Now these berries though they look similar to those that grow on the rowan tree we all know so well in our own countryside, possess certain secret qualities because they come from the 'Other-world.' An old and wrinkled man who tastes them immediately regains his youthful appearance even though he may be very old. It is the same for an old woman. The most deformed young girl has just to eat three of the berries to become the most admired and beautiful young maiden in the world.

Naturally the fairies are careful to prevent these magical berries from being lost. Every fairy is told to guard them carefully lest they fall into human hands. For the power of the fairies is not to be shared with those who would invade their peaceful kingdom and seek to make the Land of Promise their own.

However, all concern for the berries was lost on this occasion amidst the dancing and merry-making of the little people; for even when not victorious they see no reason to be sad. The sound of their revelry lasted through the long night. The next day, tired but happy, they continued their journey through the plains and forests. One carefree little fairy discovered he had several scarlet berries left in his bag. Taking out a handful as he went along he chanced to let one slip into the undergrowth of moss and ferns. On he went quite unaware of his mistake. Behind, the small berry

77

lay unnoticed in the rich brown soil of Dooros Wood.

The fairy band arrived back safely at their homeland. Several weeks and even months went by and it seemed that no one would ever realise what had happened. Indeed the loss of the berry might never have been discovered had not a fairy hunting party chosen to pass by the very spot where it had been dropped. There before them they found a slender tree that stood out from all the other trees in the wood. The tiny hunters knew it could never have sprung from any earthly seed for there on its many branches hung clusters of the fairy berries.

The news of the lone fairy tree caused much distress in the fairy kingdom. The king and queen searched their realm for the culprit whose carelessness had caused the tree to take root on mortal soil. The unfortunate fairy who had dropped the single berry was brought to the royal court. For his mistake he was formally banished to the land of giants far beyond the tall mountains. There he was ordered to stay until he could find a giant willing to go to Dooros Wood and guard the fairy tree. The queen saddened by the pitiful look on the face of her small subject, gave him a handful of berries that he could offer to the giants. The berries tasting sweeter than any honey would be a strong incentive to take on the task, for any giant who agreed to protect the tree could feast on berries just as fine from morning to night.

And so the fairy set off on his long journey. Leaving the rich, green fields of his own world he climbed up into the dark, ominous mountains that lead to the Land of the Giants. There amongst the caves and craggy slopes he had no friend to guide him on his way, no companion to help him in his task.

After walking many miles without seeing any living creature, he sat down wearily between two large boulders. It was there that a very long dark shadow suddenly fell over him shutting out the daylight. Too frightened to look up he tried to hide behind one of the stones. A loud roar echoed from one hill to the other and in the same instant an enormous hand reached down and, seizing the trembling figure, lifted him into the air.

The giant glared at the small traveller from one dark eye that glowed like a coal in the middle of his forehead. His long teeth were gritted menacingly and from a metal belt slung round his waist hung a club with iron spikes. This was Sharvan the Surly, so called because of his bad temper, which made him disliked and shunned by all in the Land of Giants. Nothing could harm Sharvan; water, fire and sword were all useless against him. The only way to kill him was by striking him three times with his own club.

'What have we here?' said Sharvan, looking curiously at the meticulously dressed figure in his grasp.

'I have come from far away to seek your help,' said the tiny fairy.

'My help,' laughed the Giant, 'but why should I help you?'

In answer the fairy took some of the berries out of his pocket and offered them to the giant. Sharvan finding the quicken berries very tasty demanded some more. 'You can have as many of the berries as you like,' said the fairy, 'if you agree to guard the tree on which they grow, from all other intruders.'

'That should be an easy task,' said Sharvan, and agreed to set off with the fairy to Dooros Wood.

The exile of the tiny fairy came to an end and the fairy race felt reassured now that Sharvan watched over their tree. The giant built himself a wooden hut nearby in which to sleep and settled happily into his new life. A branch of berries hung from his belt for him to eat whenever he wished.

The fame of the fairy tree spread far and wide and every day some adventurer came to see if he could carry away a few of the berries. Not a single day went by without the Giant slaying some daring champion. All the while he remained unwounded, for fire, water and weapon were useless against him.

Not very far away from Dooros Wood there lived at this time two orphaned princesses. The two sisters called Macha and Emer, though both very beautiful, were completely different in character. Whilst Emer was loved by all for her kind and generous nature, Macha was equally disliked for her meanness and spitefulness. One day Macha could not bear any longer to watch the looks of respect and devotion in the eyes of their friends as they looked at her sister.

Leaving the castle early in the morning while everyone else, was still asleep, she made her way to the cottage of an old woman known to be a witch. From her she obtained a small phial of a thick, clear liquid. Hurrying back to her sister's bedroom she poured the contents of the phial into the basin of water in which Emer would wash when she woke. Then she withdrew to await the results of her evil work.

Quite unaware of Macha's treachery Emer arose as the first ray of sunlight shone through her casement window. Humming gently to herself she started to bathe. But she had no sooner splashed the water on to her skin than her rosy cheeks became dark and wrinkled. No doctor in the land could cure her affliction or restore her former beauty, but she remained as kind and sweet-natured as before. She never suspected that anyone would wish to do her harm, least of all her own sister.

Most of her days she spent seated at her window looking out at the natural beauty of the green hills and woods around her home. One spring morning while gazing at the tiny flowers that were beginning to blossom on the cherry tree beneath her window, she saw a tall, dark stranger dismount at the gates.

This was Donal, the only son of a king who lived far beyond the sea. He sought hospitality and friendship on his visit to this strange land. Macha ordered the servants to prepare a magnificent feast for their guest, and Donal was at once struck by the loveliness of his hostess. Emer longed to meet the young prince too, but ashamed of her appearance she remained behind in her room, listening to the happy sounds of music and laughter from the nearby banqueting hall. All at once she was overcome with sadness and several large tears trickled down her burnished cheeks.

Beneath her window a small robin, perched on a branch of the cherry tree, looked up at the weeping princess. He longed to see the young maiden smile the way she had in times gone by.

'But I am powerless to help her,' he sighed.

'There is a way,' said a blackbird in an adjacent bush. 'If you are brave enough to try it.' In Dooros Wood there is a fairy tree and were the princess to eat just three of its magic berries, her former beauty would immediately be restored. But to obtain the berries you must get past the giant Sharvan the Surly who guards the tree by day and by night.'

'I would risk any danger to see Emer happy once more,' said the robin, as he flew to try his luck in Dooros Wood.

When the robin arrived at the fairy tree he waited patiently until a warrior came to challenge the giant. While Sharvan was engaged in deadly combat he darted unnoticed towards the branch that hung from the giant's belt and plucked three berries.

Sometime later Emer found the tasty looking berries on her window ledge. As soon as she put them into her mouth she felt a cheerful flow of spirits. Glancing at her reflection in the mirror she could not believe what she saw. There was a complete vision of the past; her delicate features appeared as perfect as before the evil spell had fallen on them.

Wondering if it was all a dream she trod silently down the wide

staircase to the hall below. The assembly of richly attired lords and ladies were chattering gaily. At the entrance of the gentle Emer a sudden hush came over them all. Whispers passed from one to another as they beheld the clear form of the princess. Emer's recovery became the cause of great rejoicing.

Donal danced and talked to the princess whom he had failed to meet before. Within a short time he realised that his feelings for Macha were nothing compared to the great love he felt for Emer. Macha in a terrible rage departed from the castle never to be seen again. Emer and Donal soon decided to marry, to the joy of all, especially the robin of the cherry tree, the author of their good fortunes.

Sharvan the Surly continued to guard the fairy tree from mortal men until the coming of Diarmuid and Grainne. Grainne had heard of the magic berries and had a great desire to taste them. Diarmuid, who did not wish to refuse her anything, agreed to challenge the Giant. Wiser than any of the other champions before him, he pushed Sharvan to the ground and seized the heavy club from his hand. With three mighty blows he slew the Giant that had watched over the fairy tree for so long.

The Fairy Thorn

BY SIR SAMUEL FERGUSON

'Get up, our Anna dear, from the weary spinning-wheel;
  For your father's on the hill, and your mother is asleep;
Come up above the crags, and we'll dance a highland-reel
  Around the fairy thorn on the steep.'

At Anna Grace's door 'twas thus the maidens cried,
  Three merry maidens fair in kirtles of the green;
And Anna laid the rock and the weary wheel aside,
  The fairest of the four, I ween.

They're glancing through the glimmer of the quiet eve,
  Away in milky wavings of neck and ankle bare;
The heavy-sliding stream in its sleepy song they leave,
  And the crags in the ghostly air:

And linking hand in hand, and singing as they go,
  The maids along the hill-side have ta'en their fearless way,
Till they come to where the rowan trees in lonely beauty grow
  Beside the Fairy Hawthorn gray.

The Hawthorn stands between the ashes tall and slim,
  Like matron with her twin grand-daughters at her knee;
The rowan berries cluster o'er her low head gray and dim
  In ruddy kisses sweet to see.

The merry maidens four have ranged them in a row,
  Between each lovely couple a stately rowan stem,
And away in mazes wavy, like skimming birds they go,
  Oh never caroll'd bird like them!

But solemn is the silence of the silvery haze
  That drinks away their voices in echoless repose,
And dreamily the evening has still'd the haunted braes
  And dreamier the gloaming grows.

83

And sinking one by one, like lark-notes from the sky
  When the falcon's shadow saileth across the open shaw,
Are hush'd the maiden's voices as cowering down they lie
  In the flutter of their sudden awe.

For, from the air above, and the grassy ground beneath,
  And from the mountain ashes and the old Whitethorn between,
A power of faint enchantment doth through their beings breathe,
  And they sink down together on the green.

They sink together silent, and stealing side by side,
  They fling their lovely arms o'er their drooping necks so fair,
Then vainly strive again their naked arms to hide,
  For their shrinking necks again are bare.

Thus clasp'd and prostrate all, with their heads together bow'd,
  Soft o'er their bosom's beating – the only human sound –
They hear the silky footsteps of the silent fairy crowd,
  Like a river in the air, gliding round.

No scream can any raise, no prayer can any say,
  But wild, wild, the terror of the speechless three –
For they feel fair Anna Grace drawn silently away,
  By whom they dare not look to see.

They feel their tresses twine with her parting locks of gold,
  And the curls elastic falling as her head withdraws;
They feel her sliding arms from their tranced arms unfold,
  But they may not look to see the cause;

For heavy on their senses the faint enchantment lies
  Through all that night of anguish and perilous amaze;
And neither fear nor wonder can ope their quivering eyes,
  Or their limbs from the cold ground raise.

Till out of night the earth has roll'd her dewy side,
  With every haunted mountain and streamy vale below;
When, as the mist dissolves in the yellow morning tide,
  The maidens' trance dissolveth so.

Then fly the ghastly three as swiftly as they may,
    And tell their tale of sorrow to anxious friends in vain –
They pined away and died within the year and day,
    And ne'er was Anna Grace seen again.

The Son of Bad Counsel

RETOLD BY MARY McGARRY

This story is based on a tale composed in mixed prose and verse by Brian Dhu O'Reilly who was living in Cavan in the year 1725.

he Son of Bad Counsel was a fickle and whimsical fellow. He seldom stayed long enough in any one place to call it his home. However much he might praise the fine landscape of a region, it was no hardship for him to leave it behind. Unfortunately it was the same with people. When he had the good luck to meet with and win the affections of the loveliest of maidens, though he dedicated many verses to her, their courtship was fleeting. Soon he was off down the long road once more.

One dark and stormy evening he sought shelter in the castle of a *Gruagach* or giant. On entering he was brought before the master, a strong and powerful figure, clad in silken robes and enthroned on a large, regal chair. Beside him sat his daughter, whose appearance was such as would steal the heart of any man. Her eyes were grey and thoughtful and her golden, curling locks hung down on either side of her gentle oval face. An exquisitely embroidered robe was draped over her slim shoulders and clasped on her breast with a large golden brooch.

The Son of Bad Counsel was not a little daunted by the strange surroundings in which he found himself. At last he plucked up the courage to address his host.

'King of the globe, fair is this place which I have come to;
A royal fort, white-boarded and erected as the abode of Maeve
Like unto the Dun Aileach, it is similar to Paradise,
And I am certain that it is in a court I am truly.
More delightful is this sight than Tara and Naas together,
And than the three branches in Emania, once held by the hero Dairg,
My journey I arrest till I know who dwells here.

86

The richly dressed Gruagach replied, 'It is a long time since we have had such pleasant company. For several months now we have been expecting you as we have no children or heirs, save the daughter you see before you, whom we have raised to be a wife and companion to you.'

The Son of Bad Counsel showed no surprise on hearing this; 'I would have gone to the four corners of the globe for just such a sweet maiden,' he exclaimed grandly.

At this the Gruagach rose to his feet, and looking down at his guest, offered him his chair. Then he began to describe his troubles and the help he needed from his future son-in-law before he could take the hand of his daughter in marriage.

It seemed that Magic Fog, a fairy chief residing at Dun Aoilig, because he had no children of his own to inherit his power, had kidnapped the two sons of the king of 'The Isle of the Living'. Ruan Luimneach, a mighty fairy leader, living near 'The Isle of the Living' called on all his subjects in the Western World to come to the aid of his neighbour. A plan was made to attack the stronghold of the Fog chief and rescue the two boys. Magic Fog on being informed of this had summoned his own allies. The Gruagach was one of these.

'A large part of my army has already set out for Dun Aoilig' he explained. 'Anticipating your arrival I waited behind, but now the two of us can depart together at daybreak. If you prove your bravery you shall marry my daughter on your return. If you fall in battle, we shall raise a mound above your bones, engrave your deeds on an *ogham** stone and sing your lament.'

The Son of Bad Counsel was filled with apprehension. He realized he would have to risk his life to win the fairy maiden. He began to shake with fear. The Gruagach noticing his distress asked his wife to bring them the goblet of comfort and forgetfulness. A drink from this goblet erased all cares and troubles and even if a thousand people were to sup from it, the level of the goblet would never become any lower.

His courage renewed, the Son of Bad Counsel, once more asked the name of his host.

'I am the Giant of the Unfrequented Land,' replied the Gruagach 'and this is Uncertain Castle.'

A carved wooden table was brought before them and they began a game of backgammon with the finest ivory dice. But the

---

*Oghams are characters of the Ancient Irish alphabet.

attention of the Son of Bad Counsel was so distracted by the presence of the Giant's beautiful daughter at the other side of the room, that he soon lost the game.

After a magnificent feast, as good as any presented at Tara of the Kings, the company retired to bed. In the dark passages of the Castle, the young man's fear of the following day returned. Though the fairy maiden had told him not to worry for all the fairy darts could not harm a baptised man, he still did not feel reassured. Sleep became impossible the more he thought of what the morning might bring. Finally in despair he decided to ask the one he loved to escape with him from Uncertain Castle, the Gruagach, Magic Fog and all the others in this frightening world.

Getting up, he made his way over to the large oak panelled door through which he had entered the bed chamber just a short time before. But on opening it he found himself in a cold and lonely place. The cries and bellows of wild animals issued from the dense forest and undergrowth surrounding him on all sides; he knew he was in a trap. Like a madman he tore through the trees, not stopping for breath until he reached a wide empty plain.

There in the centre rose a high green hill, a place of refuge from the terrifying beasts who might be on his trail. Up he climbed, glancing back nervously from time to time. Near the summit his way was barred by a low circular ridge around which there was no path. He was at the edge of a tempestuous inland sea, whose boiling, foaming waters splashing against the shore burnt the skin on his face and hands. But this treacherous stretch of water was his only escape route.

In a tiny harbour lay a battered boat which he tried to repair. With the noise from the forest getting louder every minute, he put to sea as fast as he could. Incessant winds bore the small craft first up on the crest of the waves, then down into the dark caverns of the earth. The Son of Bad Counsel cried out in terror. The Gruagach was awoken by his shouts and told his daughter to light a candle.

Down in the cellar they found the Son of Bad Counsel seated on a cullender covering a cask of strong new beer. This was the sea of boiling water. The roaring of boars, wolves and other animals was merely the shrieks of two cats which the sleep-walker had disturbed. The storm was nothing but the rush of breeze through an open window.

The Gruagach laughed heartily.

'You certainly won't win my daughter sitting on a cullender in a barrel of beer,' he chuckled. Filled with shame and beer, the young man returned to bed.

His dreams were even worse this time. He awoke with the fear of death at the thought of the gathering at Dun Aoilig. Leaving his bed, he went towards the door of the maiden's room to persuade her to flee with him. It opened onto a wild overgrown field. Just a few hundred yards away a large black beast was rushing in his direction. The Son of Bad Counsel leapt towards the edge of the field, where he was forced to halt by a turbulent, winding river. He did not know what to do as he was unable to swim. But preferring to take his chances in the current rather than face the monster at his heels, he dived into the dangerous waters. Though he splashed out vigorously with both his arms, he was slowly drawn down into a deep pool, thick with mud and reeds. He was sure he would drown. With water coming out of his mouth, he gave a shrill cry.

From what seemed like a long way away came the voices of the Gruagach and his daughter.

'Do you want a bath?' asked the Gruagach with a smile. 'If so we can offer you cleaner water than you'll find in the pig's food.'

To his great embarrassment the Son of Bad Counsel became aware that he was lying in a large trough filled with water and grain. The wild beast of the field was but a grunting pig. Feeling even greater shame, the poor fellow went back to try and get a couple of hours rest before the dreaded battle. The Gruagach had told him he would get the horses ready for the journey.

Despite his love for the beautiful maiden, the Son of Bad Counsel found it impossible to conquer his fear. As he tossed and turned on the bed, mumbling 'I do not want to die, I do not want to die,' a raw grey light fell on his eyes. He found himself shivering, stretched out on the dry grass of a moat, with his coat as a pillow beneath his head. Gone were the dark castle and all its inhabitants. The only sound to be heard was the chirping of a small bird perched on a bush nearby.

Through the length and breadth of Ireland, he searched for the *Sidhe* woman, who had captured his imagination. At the end of a year and a day he arrived again at the same spot where he had discovered the Castle of Uncertainty on the previous occasion. In his sleep beneath the open sky, he had a vision of his fairy love. Her gentle voice told him to stop seeking her as her father had

forced her to take another for her husband.

The next day his soul was free from the fairy spell of enchantment. From that time forth he was a reformed man; he became the Son of Good Counsel.

The Lady of Gollerus

BY T. CROFTON CROKER

On the shore of Smerwick harbour, one fine summer's morning, just at day-break, stood Dick Fitzgerald 'shoghing the dudeen', which may be translated, smoking his pipe. The sun was gradually rising behind the lofty Brandon, the dark sea was getting green in the light, and the mists, clearing away out of the valleys, went rolling and curling like the smoke from the corner of Dick's mouth.

'"Tis just the pattern of a pretty morning', said Dick, taking the pipe from between his lips, and looking towards the distant ocean, which lay as still and tranquil as a tomb of polished marble.

'Well, to be sure,' continued he, after a pause, 'tis mighty lonesome to be talking to one's self by way of company, and not to have another soul to answer one – nothing but the child of one's own voice, the echo! I know this, that if I had the luck, or maybe the misfortune,' said Dick with a melancholy smile, 'to have the woman, it would not be this way with me! – and what in the wide world is a man without a wife? He's no more surely than a bottle without a drop of drink in it, or dancing without music, or the left leg of a scissors, or a fishing line without a hook, or any other matter that is no ways complete. – Is it not so?' said Dick Fitzgerald, casting his eyes towards a rock upon the strand, which, though it could not speak, stood up as firm and looked as bold as ever Kerry witness did.

But what was his astonishment at beholding, just at the foot of that rock a beautiful young creature combing her hair, which was of a sea-green colour, and now the salt water shining on it, appeared, in the morning light, like melted butter upon cabbage.

Dick guessed at once that she was a Merrow, although he had never seen one before, for he spied the *cohuleen driuth*, or little enchanted cap, which the sea people use for diving down into the ocean, lying upon the strand, near her; and he had heard, that if once he could possess himself of the cap, she would lose the power of going away into the water. So he seized it with all

speed, and she, hearing the noise, turned her head about as natural as any Christian.

When the Merrow saw that her little diving-cap was gone, the salt tears – doubly salt, no doubt, from her – came trickling down her cheeks, and she began a low mournful cry with just the tender voice of a new-born infant. Dick, although he knew well enough what she was crying for, determined to keep the cohuleen driuth, let her cry never so much, to see what luck would come out of it. Yet he could not help pitying her, and when the dumb thing looked up in his face, and her cheeks all moist with tears, 'twas enough to make any one feel, let alone Dick, who had ever and always, like most of his countrymen, a mighty tender heart of his own.

'Don't cry, my darling,' said Dick Fitzgerald; but the Merrow, like any bold child, only cried the more for that.

Dick sat himself down by her side, and took hold of her hand, by way of comforting her. 'Twas in no particular an ugly hand, only there was a small web between the fingers, as there is in a duck's foot, but 'twas as thin and as white as the skin between egg and shell.

'What's your name, my darling?' says Dick, thinking to make her conversant with him, but he got no answer, and he was certain sure now, either that she could not speak, or did not understand him. He therefore squeezed her hand in his, as the only way he had of talking to her. It's the universal language; and there's not a woman in the world, be she fish or lady, that does not understand it.

The Merrow did not seem much displeased at this mode of conversation and, making an end of her whining all at once 'Man,' says she, looking up in Dick Fitzgerald's face, 'Man, will you eat me?'

'By all the red petticoats and check aprons between Dingle and Tralee,' cried Dick, jumping up in amazement, 'I'd as soon eat myself, my jewel! Is it I eat you, my pet? – Now 'twas some ugly ill-looking thief of a fish put that notion into your own pretty head, with the nice green hair down upon it, that is so cleanly combed out this morning!'

'Man,' said the Merrow, 'what will you do with me, if you won't eat me?'

Dick's thoughts were running on a wife. He saw, at the first glimpse, that she was handsome; but since she spoke, and spoke too like any real woman, he was fairly in love with her. 'Twas the

94

neat way she called him 'man', that settled the matter entirely.

'Fish,' says Dick, trying to speak to her after her own short fashion; 'fish,' says he, 'here's my word, fresh and fasting, for you this blessed morning, that I'll make you Mistress Fitzgerald before all the world, and that's what I'll do.'

'Never say the word twice,' says she; 'I'm ready and willing to be yours, Mister Fitzgerald; but stop, if you please, 'till I twist up my hair.'

It was some time before she had settled it entirely to her liking, for she guessed, I suppose, that she was going among strangers, where she would be looked at. When that was done, the Merrow put the comb in her pocket, and then bent down her head and whispered some words to the water that was close to the foot of the rock.

Dick saw the murmur of the words upon the top of the sea, going out towards the wide ocean, just like a breath of wind rippling along, and says he in the greatest wonder, 'Is it speaking you are, my darling, to the salt water?'

'It's nothing else,' says she, quite carelessly, 'I'm just sending word home to my father, not to be waiting breakfast for me; just to keep him from being uneasy in his mind.'

'And who's your father, my duck?' says Dick.

'What!' said the Merrow, 'did you never hear of my father? He's the king of the waves, to be sure!'

'And yourself, then, is a real king's daughter?' said Dick, opening his two eyes to take a full and true survey of his wife that was to be. 'Oh, I'm nothing else but a made man with you, and a king your father – to be sure he has all the money that's down in the bottom of the sea!'

'Money,' repeated the Merrow, 'what's money?'

'''Tis no bad thing to have when one wants it,' replied Dick, 'and maybe now the fishes have the understanding to bring up whatever you bid them?'

'Oh! yes,' said the Merrow, 'they bring me what I want''

'To speak the truth, then,' said Dick, ''tis a straw bed I have at home before you, and that I'm thinking, is no ways fitting for a king's daughter. So, if 'twould not be displeasing to you, just to mention, a nice feather-bed, with a pair of new blankets – but what am I talking about? Maybe you have not such things as beds down under the water?'

'By all means,' said she, 'Mr. Fitzgerald – plenty of beds at your service. I've fourteen oyster-beds of my own, not to mention one just planting for the rearing of young ones.'

'You have?' says Dick, scratching his head and looking a little puzzled. '"Tis a feather-bed I was speaking of – but clearly, yours is the very cut of a decent plan, to have bed and supper so handy to each other, that a person when they'd have the one, need never ask for the other.'

However, bed or no bed, money or no money, Dick Fitzgerald determined to marry the Merrow, and the Merrow had given her consent. Away they went, therefore, across the strand, from Gollerus to Ballinrunnig, where Father Fitzgibbon happened to be that morning.

'There are two words to this bargain, Dick Fitzgerald,' said his Reverence, looking mighty glum. 'And is it a fishy woman you'd marry? – the Lord preserve us! – send the scaly creature home to her own people, that's my advice to you, wherever she came from.'

Dick had the cohuleen driuth in his hand, and was about to give it back to the Merrow, who looked covetously at it, but he thought for a moment, and then, says he, 'Please your Reverence, she's a king's daughter.'

'If she was the daughter of fifty kings,' said Father Fitzgibbon, 'I tell you, you can't marry her, she being a fish.'

'Please your Reverence,' said Dick again in an undertone, 'she is as mild and as beautiful as the moon.'

'If she was as mild and as beautiful as the sun, moon, and stars, all put together, I tell you, Dick Fitzgerald,' said the Priest, stamping his right foot, 'you can't marry her, she being a fish!'

'But she has all the gold that's down in the sea only for the asking, and I'm a made man if I marry her; and,' said Dick, looking up slily, 'I can make it worth anyone's while to do the job.'

'Oh! that alters the case entirely,' replied the Priest. 'Why there's some reason now in what you say: why didn't you tell me this before? Marry her by all means if she was ten times a fish. Money, you know, is not to be refused in these bad times, and I may as well have the use of it as another, that maybe would not take half the pains in counselling you as I have done.'

So Father Fitzgibbon married Dick Fitzgerald to the Merrow, and like any loving couple, they returned to Gollerus well pleased with each other. Everything prospered with Dick – he was at the sunny side of the world. The Merrow made the best of wives, and they lived together in the greatest contentment.

It was wonderful to see, considering where she had been

brought up, how she would busy herself about the house, and how well she nursed the children; for at the end of three years there were as many young Fitzgeralds – two boys and a girl.

In short, Dick was a happy man, and so he might have continued to the end of his days, if he had only the sense to take proper care of what he had got; many another man, however, beside Dick, has not had wit enough to do that.

One day when Dick was obliged to go to Tralee, he left his wife minding the children at home after him and thinking she had plenty to do without disturbing his fishing tackle.

Dick was no sooner gone than Mrs Fitzgerald set about cleaning up the house and, chancing to pull down a fishing-net, what should she find behind it in a hole in the wall but her own cohuleen driuth.

She took it out and looked at it, and then she thought of her father the king, and her mother the queen, and her brothers and sisters, and she felt a longing to go back to them. She sat down on a little stool and thought over the happy days she had spent under the sea; then she looked at her children, and thought on the love and affection of poor Dick, and how it would break his heart to lose her. 'But,' says she, 'he won't lose me entirely, for I'll come back to him again; and who can blame me for going to see my father and my mother, after being so long away from them.'

She got up and went towards the door, but came back again to look once more at the child that was sleeping in the cradle. She kissed it gently, and as she kissed it, a tear trembled for an instant in her eye and then fell on its rosy cheek. She wiped away the tear, and turning to the eldest little girl, told her to take good care of her brothers, and to be a good child herself, until she came back. The Merrow then went down to the strand.

The sea was lying calm and smooth, just heaving and glittering in the sun, and she thought she heard a faint sweet singing, inviting her to come down. All her old ideas and feelings came flooding over her mind, Dick and her children were at the instant forgotten, and placing the cohuleen driuth on her head, she plunged in.

Dick came home in the evening and, missing his wife, he asked Kathelin, his little girl, what had become of her mother, but she could not tell him. He then inquired of the neighbours, and he learned that she was seen going towards the strand with a strange-looking thing liked a cocked hat in her hand. He returned to his cabin to search for the cohuleen driuth. It was gone, and the truth now flashed upon him.

Year after year did Dick Fitzgerald wait, expecting the return of his wife, but he never saw her more. Dick never married again, always thinking that the Merrow would sooner or later return to him, and nothing could ever persuade him but that her father the king kept her below by main force; 'For,' said Dick, 'she surely would not of herself give up her husband and her children.'

While she was with him, she was so good a wife in every respect, that to this day she is spoken of in the tradition of the country as the pattern for one, under the name of 'The Lady of Gollerus'.

The White Hen

RETOLD BY MARY McGARRY

Once upon a time there lived, in the kingdom of Kerry, an old woman who had one daughter called Mary. Now, this Mary being as pretty a girl as you'd meet in a day's walk was much admired and sought after by the young men of the district. She, however, cared for none of them. Nevertheless, the old woman, who besides being rather short-tempered was also very poor, thought she would turn her daughter's conquests to good account.

Accordingly, when her small field of potatoes was ready for digging, she asked eight of her daughter's most devoted admirer's to come and dig it, 'for the love of Mary'. Twice as many volunteered and the old woman, delightedly, picked out the ten strongest. Each of these arrived for work manfully at six o'clock the following morning and as they began their labour the mother set about making an oatmeal stirabout for their breakfast.

When the meal was ready she told Mary to put it out into the large wooden dishes she had borrowed for the occasion. Bidding the young girl to take only the scrapings from the pot for her own breakfast, the old woman went out to call the men from their work. The field being some distance from their cabin, this took her a considerable time. In the meanwhile, having served out the required number of portions Mary sat down to enjoy the very meagre remains that had been alloted to her. Her hunger was far from satisfied, for not only had she an extremely healthy appetite, but the evening before her mother, in some fit of ill humour, had sent her to bed without her supper. The temptation of the steaming bowls of stirabout on the table before her was too great. She approached the first portion and looking wistfully at it, exclaimed,

'Dan O'Brien is mighty fond of me — I'm sure he'd never grudge me this bowl of stirabout!'

At that she dipped her spoon into the mixture and in a moment devoured the whole of poor Dan O'Brien's breakfast. Her appetite seeming to increase rather than diminish, she helped herself to the next share, belonging to an equally ardent admirer, who, she persuaded herself, would be more than happy to offer it to her. In short she made a complete tour of the table and to show that she had the same high opinion of each lover, every one of their dishes she left clean as if newly washed and emptied every measure of buttermilk beside each place. Only before her mother's portion did she hesitate. But, at length, saying, 'Sure it would be a shame to make a stranger of my own mother,' she sent this the way of the rest.

She had barely finished her fine meal, when the old woman returned, followed by the ten hard-working lads, all set to do justice to whatever was placed before them. But what were they confronted by but a row of empty dishes!

'What has happened to the breakfast?' demanded the old woman furiously. Mary stated simply that she had eaten it and explained her reasons for doing so. The mother was dumbfounded. The suitors, of course, declared, one and all, that Mary was more than welcome to the food and they were quite happy to do without any breakfast. Without any complaint they made their way back to the potato field. But this may have been no more than simple politeness. In fact, within a short time, several proved that this was the case by marrying other girls, who if not as pretty as Mary, at least had half her appetite!

As soon as the would-be suitors were out of sight and hearing, the old woman flew at her unfortunate daughter and in the most awful rage dragged her by her long, raven coloured hair out of the cabin. Despite all her pleas and promises, the poor girl received a merciless beating for satisfying her appetite. How long the mother might have continued to punish her daughter is hard to say. She was interrupted by the arrival of a gentleman, richly dressed, riding a fine white horse and followed by two grooms in splendid liveries and well mounted. Leaping from his horse, he seized the stick with which the old woman was striking the girl and asked why she was treating such a lovely, young creature in so cruel a manner.

'What's that to you?' snapped the old woman. 'You should mind your own business and I'll mind mine — that way we'll both be better off.'

The gentleman on hearing this, lifted Mary up into his arms and springing back in the saddle, he said, 'Now, my old dame, unless you give an immediate and satisfactory answer to my question you'll never see me or this fair girl again.'

The old woman frightened by this show of strength by one who appeared to be a very great man indeed, replied in a much subdued tone, 'If you must know then, I beat her because she knitted two pairs of stockings, while another would be knitting one pair.'

'Fie on you,' said the gentleman, 'that's no reason to punish her. If she did nothing worse than that I'll take her with me, for I see you're not fit to take care of her.'

'Oh dear, sir,' cried the old woman, 'leave her to me and I'll tell you the truth this time. I beat her for spinning too fast. When I left her with enough flax to keep her busy for ten hours, she had it spun in two.'

'That gave you no right to beat her,' said the gentleman, 'on the contrary, you ought to have been proud to have such a fine spinner in your home. You don't deserve to have the like of her for a daughter, so, if she chooses, she shall come with me.'

'Oh yes, yes,' cried Mary, who knew her mother too well not to dread being left alone with her again.

The gentleman was more than half way down the road on his fine steed, when the old woman cried after him in desperation, 'Stop, stop and you shall hear the real truth!'

But it was too late. Ignoring her cries, the gentleman set spur to his horse and disappeared into the distance with Mary and the two grooms.

They rode on and on, until at last they came to a grand house, with a fine park around it. This was the estate of a powerful native Irishman called MacElligott. Welcoming Mary, he declared that this could become her home too if she agreed to marry him. Mary being a wise young woman did not wait to be asked twice, but immediately consented to be his wife. MacElligott shortly led the young country girl, clad in delicate lace and the most expensive jewels, into the chapel to be wed. So beautiful did she look that everyone whispered that she must surely be some great princess in disguise.

The large house was filled to overflowing with guests from all around and the celebrations went on for many days. All the chiefs of Kerry and from as far away as Cork, Limerick and Clare came to pay their respects to the fair bride, who behaved as properly as if she had been born to rule. Before the end of the week MacElligot received a visit from his brother who lived near Tralee, and had himself recently got married to a daughter of MacGillicuddy of the Reeks.

The two young women got on so well together, that when the

rest of the company had departed, MacElligott pressed his brother who was known as MacElligott Beag, to stay a few days longer. It was an unlucky hour for Mary when they agreed to do so. That evening as the two brothers were sitting together after dinner, it happened that they began to talk about their wives. As the wine stimulated their conversation, MacElligott more than a little unkindly began to praise Mary and make little of his brother's wife. After a time, the brother became extremely irritated as well he might.

'I grant you,' he said 'that Mary has a prettier face and neater figure than Aideen, but I'll bet you a thousand pounds in gold that Aideen will spin more in two hours than Mary will do in ten, and that's worth more in a wife than good looks.'

At that MacElligott remembered what the old woman had said about Mary's spinning.

'Done,' he cried, 'and I think you're caught now, for Mary's as fine a spinner as any in the kingdom of Kerry, and you'll lose your money.'

Now in those days it was only the great ladies of the land that knew how to spin and they in turn instructed their handmaidens. As the brother was aware that Mary was just a poor woman's daughter, he was quite sure she had little knowledge of the craft. This, of course, was the case, but off went the two men to inform their wives of the wager. Aideen got up quite happily from where she was sitting and went to fetch her spinning wheel. It was of ebony, inlaid with silver, and had been the wedding gift of her grandmother.

MacElligot turned to his own wife, who was in a complete state of confusion at the announcement. Not having the courage to confess the truth and admit that she knew absolutely nothing about spinning, she exclaimed in a faint voice that she had no spinning wheel.

'That problem is soon solved,' said her husband and he sent one of her attendants to fetch his mother's spinning wheel from a large chest in the corner of the grand hall. This wheel was even finer than that owned by Aideen, for made of Irish oak, it was studded with Kerry diamonds and Wicklow gold. Mary's heart sank at the sight of it, and her only remaining hope was that the good-natured Aideen, once she had confided in her, would help her in the task. However, in this too she was disappointed. The two MacElligotts arranged that each lady should be shut up alone in separate turrets for two hours. At the end of this time whichever had spun the most would be declared the winner.

Enclosed in a tiny turret, Mary cast aside the useless spinning wheel and throwing herself upon the floor wept bitterly. Her tears continued to flow, until she was roused by a gentle tapping at the window. Glancing up she was surprised to see, on the outside sill, a beautiful white hen, pressing her beak against the frame of the window. As soon as Mary opened the window, in flew the White Hen.

'Good day, Bean MacElligott,'* said the White Hen. 'Pray what are you crying for?' So upset was the poor lady that she did not stop to wonder how a hen could address her thus, and merely replied that there was nothing that could be done to help her.

'How do you know that?' said the White Hen. 'Tell me your trouble first, and then I'll tell you whether I can help you or not.' Mary relieved to have someone to talk to told her the whole sad tale.

'I'll help you,' said the White Hen, 'I'll complete your task for you, but you must do one thing for me in return.'

'What's that?' said Mary, 'I'd go to the world's end for you if you save me now.'

'That's not what I want at all,' said the White Hen. 'What I want is, for you to find out my name. I'll be back with you in a year and a day from now, and if you can't tell me my name then, you must consent to be my property, to do what I please with.'

A year and a day seemed a long time to Mary and, never doubting that somehow she would discover the hen's name, she agreed to be bound by this condition. At that the White Hen shook her wings and down on the floor dropped a dozen little white chickens who, flying to the spinning wheel, in less than five minutes completed the whole of Mary's task.

While Mary was delightedly expressing her gratitude the White Hen gathered her chickens again under her wings and saying 'Farewell Bean MacElligott, in a year and a day we meet again', flew out of the window.

Mary having examined the work and satisfied herself that it was well done, arranged her disordered dress and hair, washed the traces of tears from her eyes and sat down to await the coming of the two brothers. At the appointed hour, MacElligot was extremely proud to find Mary had performed her task so well, whilst his brother's wife was still bending over her wheel with less than

---

*'Bean' is the Gaelic for 'Mrs.'

half as much completed. In point of fact, Aideen had done wonders but could not compete with the fairy power of the White Hen. In great disappointment MacElligot Beag cast down one thousand guineas in payment of his lost wager and stormed out of the house with his wife and train.

For some time Mary enjoyed the pleasures of her new life. But as the year progressed she became more and more concerned about her agreement with the White Hen. One day when returning from a hunting party with her husband she caught sight of a remarkable white hen at a cottage door. Getting down from her horse, she called to the woman who stood curtseying in the doorway, 'Pray, what is the name of that white hen?'

The enquiry was futile for the hen had no name and all present including her husband laughed at her question. Mary's anxiety increased and soon she was surveying all the hens in the neighbourhood, regardless of whether they were white or not. Only after much fruitless searching did she give up the vain attempt to discover the name of her feathered visitor. Sadly she realized that the hen was nothing other than a malignant fairy who sought to entrap her. A hundred times a day she rebuked herself for the deceit which was the cause of her entanglement with the White Hen, but the damage was done.

When MacElligott was at home Mary tried to appear gay and unconcerned, but in his absence she gave way to extremes of depression and would pass many days in her room silently weeping over her approaching fate. Now it happened that there was an old servant in the house called Conor who was very attached to the MacElligott family and had taken a particular interest in the well-being of the young bride. Though no one else seemed aware of it, he noticed how pale she had become and guessed there was some deep-rooted reason for her unhappiness. One morning when the master had just departed on a week's hunting trip, he came to see Mary in her apartment. He pressed her to confide in him the cause of her distress, hoping that he might be able to assist her in some way. Mary, who for a long time had needed just such sympathy, told him the whole story from beginning to end. When she had finished Conor asked when the time would be up.

'There are but two days more, this is Tuesday and I have until Thursday afternoon at three o'clock' she said, bursting into tears.

Conor told her not to despair and set off in search of the White Hen, promising to return with her name by Thursday or not return at all. Yet he was not blind to the difficulties of such an undertaking. The very first clutch of fowls he came to, he stopped to examine. A fine white hen caught his attention and as he stood staring at it, the woman of the house asked him if he would like to know the name of the bird.

'Indeed I would,' replied Conor, eagerly.

'Well,' said the woman smiling, 'the children call her Bean MacElligott, because the young mistress is so curious about her.'

Not discouraged, Conor travelled on, halting at every cabin on his way. He asked those he met whether they knew anything of the White Hen. When old friends offered him hospitality he refused it, afraid to delay for any length of time. Not till it became too dark to go any further did he take a few hours rest on a cabin floor. At daybreak he arose and was off again.

By the following evening he found himself weary and dispirited not far from the entrance to a thick forest. At a tiny, rocky stream, he bent down to quench his thirst and then sat back to review the situation.

'I greatly fear I'm on a fool's errand,' he said to himself. 'I am never going to discover the name of that hen in time to save my mistress. It's an impossible task as old Sean, the fairy man, died last Easter and there isn't another knowledgeable man or woman in the whole country round!'

'Don't be too sure of that, Conor O'Callaghan,' said a voice, so near that it startled him. Turning round he saw, just at his elbow, a little old man, dressed in a loose frieze great-coat, fastened round his waist with a leather belt. On his head he had an odd sort of high peaked hat.

'How on earth did you get here,' said Conor.

'Never mind how I came here,' said the old man. 'You said their was not a knowledgeable man in the country and now with one before your very eyes you haven't the sense to put a question to him.'

'Why, many thanks,' said Conor, 'I wonder if you can tell me the name of the White Hen that came to Bean MacElligott, and a blessing on you if you can.'

'What will you give me to tell you?' asked the old man.

'Anything,' replied Conor, 'anything you want provided you give me the name.'

'All I ask is that you sign this piece of parchment I have here with the blood from a vein in your left arm.'

Eager to help his mistress, Conor was about to pierce the vein when he suddenly thought to look over what was written on the parchment. When he discovered that by signing it he would be selling his soul to the old man, he threw the awful document to the ground in horror. The old man at once disappeared in a flash of fire, leaving behind a smell of burning sulphur, so strong that it nearly choked Conor, who fell fainting to the ground.

By the time he recovered his senses darkness had fallen and all was silent around him. He proceeded on his way, thankful for his escape from the evil spirit that had tried to ensnare him. Once he entered the wood his pace became much slower than before as he stumbled over the hidden roots of trees and knocked into projecting branches. It must have been far into the night, when at last he reached a more open spot, and exhausted sat down on a mossy and ivy-grown rock. Here he was resting when, all of a sudden, a ray of light gleamed through a crevice in the rock and, he heard the sound of voices from beneath. Hardly breathing, he listened attentively as these words floated up to his ears:

'Rejoice, rejoice, my children dear!
Tomorrow, brings Bean MacElligott here;
We'll make her our prize,
We'll mock at her sighs,
We'll peck out her eyes!

In her heart's blood we'll dabble each pinion!
She knows not, she knows not, my name is
Tirminion!'

'At last,' whispered Conor, 'I have discovered the name of the White Hen'. Filled with joy he got up and ran back through the forest and nearly all the way home, repeating as he went the name of Tirminion, so afraid was he of forgetting it.

He reached the castle early the next morning and went immediately to his mistress's chamber, where Mary was anxiously awaiting his return.

'Did you get any news about the White Hen?' she asked frantically, as soon as her hand-maidens had left the room.

'Her name is Tirminion, my lady,' replied Conor, who was delighted to see the great look of relief that passed over Mary's face. Soon he was relating all his adventures and receiving in return the most heartfelt thanks from his grateful mistress.

When the afternoon came Mary summoned her maidens to

array her in her most splendid robes and richest jewels. Then having opened all the windows in her apartment she sat back calmly to await the arrival of the White Hen.

Precisely at three o'clock the White Hen flew into the room.

'You are welcome, ma'am,' said Mary rising politely and making a gentle curtsey.

'Indeed!' replied the Hen, glaring fiercely at her. 'I doubt if I am welcome. What is my name? Tell me that Bean MacElligott.'

'Won't you take a chair and rest for a while, ma'am,' said Mary.

'No!' cried the White Hen. 'Tell me my name, I say!'

'All in good time,' replied Mary quietly. 'Won't you first take some refreshment, a glass of wine or a piece of seed cake, perhaps?'

'I have not come to be entertained!' screamed the White Hen. 'You must tell me my name or yield yourself up to me?'

'Don't get so agitated, ma'am,' said Mary.' 'You want to know your name, why it is Tirminion, of course.'

A wild scream shook the castle walls as the terrible name was uttered. The White Hen spread her feathers violently and cursed the listener who had overheard that name, which had never been spoken to sun, moon, or stars; that had only been breathed down in the depths of the earth. Her evil intentions thwarted, she flew out the window, leaving Mary trembling but happy, knowing that she was free forever from the power of the wicked Tirminion.

Her sad experience made her determined to avoid all deceit in the future. She started by confessing the truth to her husband and, though at first he was bitterly disappointed in his wife, his love for her was such that he soon forgave her. The thousand guineas were sent back to his brother and good relations restored between the two branches of the family. As for Conor, he was provided with a large pension for the rest of his days and treated as a most valued friend by both MacElligott and his gentle wife, Mary.

The White Fairy Horse

AS REMEMBERED BY DERMOTT MacMANUS

the Gweestion is a typical east Mayo river, as it winds its way quietly between long, low stone-walled hills overlooking low-lying pastures, too often flooded, till it reaches its mother, the great Moy. Its banks are thick with wild flowers and waving water-reeds, with stretches of clean, pebbly bottom, and its meadows a home for many birds, the plaintive cries of the curlew and pilibin* dominating all.

In one place the stream widens out into a large pool, which soon gives way to a lovely stretch of clear running water over gravel, where the trout can be seen lazily feeding as though all time were before them. This bit of the river is called Coolilan, or perhaps it should be *Coolilinn*, the 'back of the pool'. Being quite shallow it was a favourite place for paddling and even bathing in hot weather, whilst when the salmon came up the poachers would be there by nights with their spears and flaming sods.

The fields were good places, too, for the lads to lark and play their rough games. But the best field of all was further up, just by the big pool, the centre of which was carefully avoided, even in a boat, as it was so deep, no one knew how deep. It had the ominous name of *Linne a Bhaite* – the 'pool of the drowning man.' As no one could swim that far under water, for all one knew it might reach down to the very depths, perhaps even to the caverns of the mysterious water-spirits, a dangerous branch of the *Sidhe*, the Fairy-folk.

One warm summer many, many years ago a group of fifteen or more lads were romping in this field, using bent sticks as hurleys to knock stones and homemade wooden balls about. They stopped for a few moments to rest and talk in a corner of the field far from the river, when suddenly one of them called out and pointed to the bank. There they saw a white horse clambering ashore from the river. It was a magnificent animal, strong and well-made, with a long white mane decorating its arched neck and a flowing white tail its muscular quarters. The lads stood

*Green plover

109

gazing in admiration. Whose could it be, was their first thought. Between them they knew every horse for miles around but no ordinary country man or farmer could own such a wonderful animal without it becoming famous everywhere. Meanwhile it took no notice of the boys, but quietly grazed, moving steadily further and further from the river as it did so.

The boys drew nearer to examine it more closely and still it took no heed of them. After a while the bolder spirits went up to it, patting its neck and withers and, as it still ignored them, they were soon feeling and admiring its legs and pasterns. Eventually one actually mounted it, but quickly slid off again and another took his place. Then another boy, rather a bully, pulled him off and got on himself. It still went on grazing, so he kicked it with his heels, when it raised its head, walked a short way and went on grazing again. Seeing his companions begin to laugh, he got angry and kicked it again as hard as he could, and this time it began to trot.

Suddenly, with a loud neigh, it swung round and began to canter, which quickly became a wild gallop as it headed straight to the river. Its rider, in alarm, tried to dismount but to his dismay found he could not, his legs seeming glued to its sides. Frantically he called for help from the other horrified and now frightened boys, but they were powerless to act as it all happened so quickly and unexpectedly. The white horse reached the bank, but instead of walking into the stream in the way it had come out, it gathered its powerful quarters under it and gave a huge leap into the air, coming down in the centre of the deep pool. It plunged in head first just like a diving man, carrying the unfortunate lad with it into the depths and still firmly locked to its sides.

The boys looked on horrified as they saw the swirling water where both horse and rider had disappeared. Soon even this vanished and all that was to be seen was the smooth water of the stream flowing quietly and endlessly as if nothing had happened, and that was the last ever seen of either horse or lad – or that ever will be as far as the lad is concerned.

This affair was, of course, discussed widely and at length all round the countryside, and so the details have come down to us. The elders and all those who were 'fey' and had psychic powers unanimously held that the lad had been carried down to the caverns of the water-spirits, there to toil eternally in their service, tending the horses in their mystic stables. And so the tradition continues. Who can tell or say 'yea' or 'nay'?

Edain the Queen

BY LADY WILDE

ow it happened that the King of Munster one day saw a beautiful girl bathing, and he loved her and made her his queen. And in all the land was no woman so lovely to look upon as the fair Edain. And the fame of her beauty came to the ears of the great and powerful chief and king of the Tuatha-de-Danann, Midar by name. So he disguised himself and went to the court of the King of Munster as a wandering bard that he might look on the beauty of Edain. And he challenged the king to a game of chess.

'Who is this man that I should play chess with him?' said the king.

'Try me,' said the stranger. 'You will find me a worthy foe.'

Then the king said, 'But the chess-board is in the queen's apartment, and I cannot disturb her.'

However, when the queen heard that a stranger had challenged the king to chess, she sent her page in with the chess-board and then came herself to greet the stranger. And Midar was so dazzled with her beauty that he could not speak, he could only gaze on her. And the queen also seemed troubled, and after a time she left them alone.

'Now, what shall we play for?' asked the king.

'Let the conquerer name the reward,' answered the stranger, 'and whatever he desires let it be granted to him.'

'Agreed', replied the monarch.

Then they played the game and the stranger won.

'What is your demand now?' cried the king. 'I have given my word that whatever you name shall be yours.'

'I demand the Lady Edain, the queen, as my reward,' replied the stranger. 'But I shall not ask you to give her up to me till this day year.' And the stranger departed.

Now the king was utterly perplexed and confounded, but he took good note of the time and, on that night just a twelvemonth after, he made a great feast at Tara for all the princes, and he placed three lines of his chosen warriors all round the palace, and

forbade any stranger to enter on pain of death. So all being secure, as he thought, he took his place at the feast with the beautiful Edain beside him, all glittering with jewels and a golden crown on her head, and the revelry went on till midnight. Just then, to his horror, the king looked up, and there stood the stranger in the middle of the hall, but no one seemed to perceive him save only the king. He fixed his eyes on the queen, and coming towards her, he struck the golden harp he had in his hand and sang in a low sweet voice:

'O Edain, wilt thou come with me
To a wonderful palace that is mine?
White are the teeth there, and black the brows,
And crimson as the mead are the lips of the lovers.

O woman, if thou comest to my proud people,
'Tis a golden crown shall circle thy head,
Thou shalt dwell by the sweet streams of my land,
And drink of the mead and wine in the arms of thy lover.'

Then he gently put his arms round the queen's waist, and drew her up from her royal throne, and went forth with her through the midst of all the guests, none hindering, and the king himself was like one in a dream, and could neither speak nor move. But when he recovered himself, then he knew that the stranger was one of the fairy chiefs of the Tuatha-de-Danann who had carried off the beautiful Edain to his fairy mansion. So he sent round messengers to all the kings of Erin that they should destroy all the forts of the hated Tuatha race, and slay and kill and let none live till the queen, his young bride, was brought back to him.

Still she came not. Then the king out of revenge ordered his men to block up all the stables where the royal horses of the Dananns were kept, that so they might die of hunger. But the horses were of noble blood, and no bars or bolts could hold them, and they broke through the bars and rushed out like the whirlwind, and spread all over the country. And the kings, when they saw the beauty of the horses, forgot all about the search for Queen Edain, and only strove how they could seize and hold as many as possible for themselves of the fiery steeds with the silver hoofs and golden bridles.

Then the king raged in his wrath, and sent for the chief of the Druids, and told him he should be put to death unless he discovered the place where the queen lay hid. So the Druid went over all Ireland, and searched, and made spells with oghams on four wands of a hazel-tree. It was revealed to him that deep down in a hill in the very centre of Ireland, Queen Edain was hidden away in the enchanted palace of Midar the fairy chief.

Then the king gathered a great army, and they circled the hill, and dug down and down till they came to the very centre. And just as they reached the gate of the fairy palace, Midar by his enchantments sent forth fifty beautiful women from the hillside, to distract the attention of the warriors, all so like the queen in form and features and dress, that the king himself could not make out truly, if his own wife were amongst them or not.

But Edain, when she saw her husband so near her, was touched by love of him in her heart, and the power of the enchantment fell from her soul, and she came to him, and he lifted her up on his horse and kissed her tenderly, and brought her back safely to his royal palace of Tara, where they lived happily ever after.

But soon after, the power of the Tuatha-de-Danann was broken for ever, and the remnant that was left took refuge in the caves where they exist to this day, and practise their magic, and work spells, and are safe from death until the judgement day.

Earl Desmond and the Banshee

ANON

'Now cheer thee on, my gallant steed,
   There's a weary way before us –
Across the mountain swiftly speed,
   For the storm is gathering o'er us'.
Away, away the horseman rides;
   His bounding steed's dark form
Seem'd o'er the soft black moss to glide –
   A spirit of the storm!

Now rolling in the troubled sky,
   The thunder's loudly crashing;
And through the dark clouds, driving by,
   The moon's pale light is flashing.
In sheets of foam the mountain flood
   Comes roaring down the glen;
On the steep bank one moment stood
   The horse and rider then.

One desperate bound the courser gave,
   And plunged into the stream;
And snorting, stemmed the boiling wave,
   By the lightning's quivering gleam.
The flood is past – the bank is gained –
   Away with headlong speed:
A fleeter horse than Desmond rein'd
   Ne'er served at lover's need.

His scatter'd train, in eager haste,
   Far, far behind him ride;
Alone he's crossed the mountain waste,
   To meet his promised bride.
The clouds across the moon's dim form
   Are fast and faster sailing,
And sounds are heard on the sweeping storm
   Of wild unearthly wailing.

At first low moanings seem'd to die
  Away, and faintly languish;
Then swell into the piercing cry
  Of deep, heart-bursting anguish.
Beneath an oak, whose branches bare
  Were crashing in the storm,
With wringing hands and streaming hair,
  There sat a female form.

To pass the oak in vain he tried;
  His steed refused to stir,
Though furious 'gainst his panting side
  Was struck the bloody spur.
The moon, by driving clouds o'ercast,
  Witheld its fitful gleam;
And louder than the tempest blast
  Was heard the Banshee's scream.

And, when the moon unveiled once more,
And showed her paly light,
Then nought was seen save the branches hoar
  Of the oak-tree's blasted might.
That shrieking form had vanished
  From out that lonely place;
And, like a dreamy vision, fled,
  Nor left one single trace.

Earl Desmond gazed – his bosom swell'd
  With grief and sad foreboding;
Then on his fiery way he held,
  His courser madly goading.
For well that wailing voice he knew,
  And onward hurrying fast,
O'er hills and dales impetuous flew,
  And reached his home at last.

Beneath his wearied courser's hoof
  The trembling drawbridge clangs,
And Desmond sees his own good roof,
  But darkness o'er it hangs.

He pass'd beneath the gloomy gate,
  No guiding tapers burn;
No vassals in the court-yard wait,
  To welcome his return.

The hearth is cold in the lonely hall,
  No banquet decks the board;
No page stands ready at the call,
  To 'tend his wearied lord.
But all within is dark and drear,
  No sights or sounds of gladness –
Nought broke the stillness on the ear,
  Save a sudden burst of sadness.

Then slowly swell'd the keener's strain
  With loud lament and weeping,
For round a corpse a mournful train
  The sad death-watch were keeping.
Aghast he stood, bereft of power,
  Hope's fairy visions fled;
His fears confirmed – his beauteous flower –
  His fair-hair'd bride – was dead!

The Harp of the Dagda Mor

BY ALICE FURLONG

O f old there were wars and conflicts between the
Fomorians or 'Men-from-under-Sea,' and the Tuatha
Dé Danaan, or Fairy-folk, who were of the gods
of Dana, as it is said.

It was at the Battle of Moytuiré that the Harp was taken. This
was the manner of it.

The dark, wicked, vengeful Fomorians were upon the one side;
the Fairy-folk of the gods of Dana upon the other. There was
ill-will and bad blood between them, on account of taxes and
tributes.

The kingship of the Island was with the Fomorians when the
Fairy-folk came there. An enchanted wind carried them – the 'Red
Wind of the Hills' it is called, and it blows unto this day, a
Sluashee, or fairy-blast. The Fomorians had no knowledge of their
coming until they saw them approaching Tara in bands and
companies. Like the rising of the sun on a morn in May was the
coming of the Tuatha De Danaan.

It is better that we should share our great Duns with them than
that they should be putting us down in the little Duns with the
stone roofs upon them,' said the wise men of the Fomorians.
The little Duns were the cairns where the dead lay in their
sleeping.

'That is a good saying,' made answer the King of the Fomorians.
He did not want to be taking treasure from his treasure-store to
reward smiths and artificers for the turning and casting of long
sharp shining spears such as the Tuatha Dé Danaan bore in their
kingly white hero-hands.

So the wise people of the Fomorians parleyed with the Fairy-
folk of the Gods of Dana. It was agreed upon that they were to
live together in Erinn like brothers in the one house.

But Bress, the King of the Fomorians, was a niggard. He took
tributes of the people, both native and stranger, and he never
gave them the shelter of his shield nor made for them a wounding
with his spear. He called his poet and law-maker to him one day,

and he said, 'Make me a law that will fill my keeves with an abundance and no stint of the best of milk, O Druid!'

The Druid made the law. The law was proclaimed to the people of Erinn. It commanded that the milk of every hairless dun cow was to be made over to Bress, the King of Tara. The people did not disturb themselves over that. The merry folk raised a laugh and the loudest laugh of all came from Munster, for there were many dun cows, and plentiful milkers, in that province, but none of them hairless.

The word of their scorn was brought to Bress. He sent for his *Filé*, or poet.

'What's this that you have done me, O Filé!' said he to him. 'You have given me a bad return for the food and drink and keeping you have had of me.'

'Not so,' said the Druid. 'Give me a swift horse that does not whinny, a charioteer that is not talkative, and a chariot with greased wheels, and let me go through the province of Munster.'

He got what he asked for, and he went through the province of Munster; with speed he passed over it in the silence and the darkness of the night. But in every pasture and every place where herds were gathered, he made a fire of ferns, and he drove through the same all the dun cows he found with the herd. Between the waxing and the waning of the moon, he went out from Tara, and returned to it.

The Munster people raised a great *ululu* when they saw what had been done. But their sorrow was joy and gladness to Bress, the King. He sent his tax-gatherers round about to every chief and every strong man of the province. The hairless dun cows were driven to Tara, and the keeves of Bress filled with an abundance and no stint of the best of milk.

That was not enough. Corpré Mac Etaine, the yellow-haired poet of the Tuatha Dé Danaan, came to the court of Tara. He was vestured for a king's company. Snow-white was the tunic upon him; his mantle glistened and shone with embroideries of gold and silver; in his slender hand he carried the poet's stave, made of the lasting red yew, and graven with the signs and symbols that were devised by the wisdom of Ogma. It was Corpré, the Filé, that could interpret the signs of Ogma on flags and staves, and read the stars, and command the minds of men in faintings and trances.

He was led to a chamber, small and dark. No pleasant fire smoked up to the roof-tree, no couch nor curtain was by the wall.

there was neither music nor good company in that chamber.
'I seek the hospitality of the King,' said the Filé, Corpré Mac Etaine. 'It has ever been my custom to grease my knife at the table of a king, and to drink bountifully of good heady ale from his royal vat. I have never yet sat to meat without the music of minstrels and the companionship of noble men and women.'
'Not such is the hospitality of this Court,' made answer the door-keeper.

The son of Etaine, yellow-haired Corpré, was left to himself for a long time, sitting on a block of wood in that dark chamber with neither fire nor light to comfort him. After that, the King's servant set before him three dry wheat-cakes, without honey or butter, or as much as a dish under them. Corpré rose up and he spoke a satire against the King of the Fomorians. This is what he said:

> No meat of swine; no flesh of deer;
> No ale; no wine; no milk of steer;
> No stories fine; no roof, night near;
> The song is mine; for Bress, the cheer.

When he had made an end of his speaking, he went out of the place. He travelled the plains of the Five Provinces, and he recited his *rann* in the hearing of the Fairy-folk of the gods of Dana. That was the first satire made in Erinn, and it is said that better was never made before nor after. They that had been living as brothers at peace in one house, then became like unto brothers in one house when there is contention for the mastery thereof.

But the folk of the gods of Dana were much skilled in magic. They laid a spell of fear upon Bress, the King, so that he rose and fled out of Tara. They put their own King, Naud, in the royal Dun; and he exercised hospitality, and bounty, and no man went hungry from his doors. But Bress betook himself to his father, Elatha. He got from him a company of warriors: dark, large, mighty men they were. Balor Balcbeimnech was the head and chief of them, the glance of one of his eyes gave death. He began to build the fortifications of Bress, in the north-west part of the island; he built them on the verge of the high, green, glassy billows of the sea. They are called 'The Giant's Causeway' to this day.

But the Tuatha Dé Danaan made their preparations in Tara. Giobniu, the smith, and Creidne, the artificer, and Lunchtine, the carpenter, fashioned for them spears, sharp and shining; javelins, grey and green; shields, round and well-turned, rimmed with red gold, and bossed with crimson and blue. When all was ready, the Druids raised a vast white mist about the whole army (so that in all Erinn no man saw the sun for the space of three days). In the cover of that fairy fog, the wise folk marched to the plain of the north, which is named Moytuiré. They were within a league of the Fomorian camp when the mist dispersed and discovered them to the watchmen of Bress. These gave the word to the great, powerful, large men. The Fomorians came together on the borders of the camp.

'I see a warrior coming towards us, driving over dark bogs and heaths,' said Indech, one of them. 'This is the appearance upon him: a star, bright and keen-pointed, shining between the day and the night; and many a lesser star is along with him.'

'That man will be Ogma, a champion of the Tuatha Dé Danaan,' made answer Bress, the King of the Fomorians.

Indech turned himself about to the right, and he said, 'I behold another warrior approaching, he comes by the margins of woods and dim branchy forests. Like to the full moon standing in the middle of the heavens, I behold him; and it is only the greater ones of his company I can espy, for his light is very brilliant and glorious.'

'That will be Lugh-lam-fada, the master of the manifold crafts,' made answer Bress. 'No small help will that man render to the side upon which he places himself; and it would better become him to be with us in this camp than in the following of Ogma, for his mother was of the Fomorians. By the oath my people swear, I wish he were upon my right hand in this battle!'

Indech turned himself about to the left, and he said, 'There is yet another warrior coming with speed over the mountains and hills. The glory of morning and evening are gathered together into one brightness to make the light that is round about him in clouds and radiant vapours! Such is the splendour of his appearance, that he is like the sun with the whole heaven to himself in the noonday!'

When he had listened to this word, there was shame and sorrow upon Bress.

'We will taste the bitterness of death before night!' said he, and he lifted his shield up against his face. 'That man will incline the beam of battle against us, and bring destruction upon us, for he is the Dagda Mor, the prime wizard and sorcerer of the Tuatha Dé Danaan!'

That was a true saying. The fight began on the Feast of Samhain: for the space of four days there were men crying out their souls on the black plain of Moytuiré. There was clashing of spear upon shield, and the noise of the whizzing of strung javelins, and tumult and clamour. The birds flew away out of the trees, and the kine would not drink of the well-waters nor the river-waters, for they were running red with the blood of men. Dark ravens and the spectres of the air screamed overhead, exulting in the flow of crimson blood from the fair white flesh of the warriors and heroes.

But when it was the evening of the fourth day, the Sword of Tethra, one of the kings of the Fomorians, fell into the hands of the Dagda Mor. The beam of battle then inclined against the Fomorians and they fled away into glens and coverts and dark places, and their countenances were pale with fear, and their knees tottered and knocked together. They left Balor Balc-beimnech a dead man upon the field, with the sling-stone of Lugh-lam-fada in his Evil Eye.

Then the Morrigan, the ancient Grey Raven of Battle, proclaimed and cried aloud to the fords and river-mouths and chief waters of Erinn, and made a vaunt of the victory of the Fairy-folk of the gods of Dana.

After that, those yellow-haired champions and heroes gathered in the banquet-hall to a feasting. And Ogma unsheathed the Sword, and made it relate to the company all its deeds and exploits: it spoke with a voice, for there was a demon hidden in the Sword. And when they had made an end of that, there was a call for music from the Harp of the Dagda Mor. But when they sought it in its own place, behold, it was not there!

'An evil thing has come to pass,' said the Dagda Mor. 'For the Fomorians have laid hands upon my sweet-tongued Harp; but it shall be a silent mouth with them, until I find it.'

Then Ogma and Lugh-lam-fada rose from their silken couches, and they said, 'If it were to be over hills of glass and lakes of smothering fire, we will fare forth with thee on that seeking.'

They took spear and shield, and they went hot-foot after the Fomorians. They were going from a night-fall to a night-fall; and they crossed nine high hills and nine dark valleys and nine broad, perilous ford-mouths before they found the Fomorians. It was eating and drinking they were, but that was a sorrowful banquet. There was neither music nor story-telling, but the heaviness of death was upon them all, both men and women.

And in the midst of them was hung the Harp of the Dagda: a silent mouth, for not even the most skilful of the Fomorian minstrels could draw music from it on account of the spells and enchantments it was under.

Of a sudden the three bright-faced heroes of the Tuatha Dé Danaan stood in the banqueting-hall. The Dagda Mor opened wide his slender willow arms. His eyes became like to sparks of lightning.

He spoke to the Harp, and he said, 'Come, Murmur of the Apple Tree! Come, Hive of Melody! Come, Summer, come, Winter, from the mouths of harps and hollows and pipes!'

The Harp sprang to him. Nine foemen rose up in its path: it gave death to the first and last of them. It leaped to the bosom of the Dagda Mor, and it was like a son running to his father, or a maid to her sweetheart. He drew his hand over the strings of the Harp, and he played the *Goltrai*, the plaintive tear-song. It was then that the dark vengeful Fomorians, both men and women, forgot their hatred and their battle-fury. The warriors drew their mantles over their countenances to hide their weeping; and the women wept three showers of tears, so heart-rending were the strains of the magic Harp.

'Give them another kind of music!' said Ogma, the champion.

'I can do that,' made answer the Dagda Mor.

Then he drew his hand over the strings, and he played the *Gentrai*, the mirthful music, until the young men and the women shouted and laughed for the delight and the joy of it. Such was its power that if every man and woman in Erinn had a father and mother lying dead before them, they would have to laugh with gladness for that melody.

'Give them the *Suantrai*, and let us be going away with ourselves!' said Lugh-lam-fada, the master of the manifold sciences.

'I can do that; none better than myself to do it,' made answer the Dagda.

Then he swept his hand over the strings of the Harp, and it answered him with the music of sleep. Creeping, crooning, soothing strains of murmurous music it played for him, until the heads of the Fomorian warriors fell down upon their breasts, and the women sank into deep and heavy slumber.

The Dagda Mor carried his Harp forth into the darkness, and returned with his companions to his own people. That was the last time there was a battle between the Fomorians and the Fairy-folk of the gods of Dana.

And the kingship and sovereignty of the island remained with those last, until the son of Miledh came over-seas, and drove them into the Raths and Shee-mounds where they live to this day, an invisible, enchanted people.

A Select Bibliography

T. Crofton Croker: *Fairy Legends and Traditions of the South of Ireland*, 1825

William Carleton: *Traits and Stories of the Irish Peasantry*, 1830

Lady Wilde: *Ancient Legends of Ireland*, 1887

D. R. McAnally: *Irish Wonders*, 1888

Samuel Lover: *Legends and Stories of the Irish Peasantry*, 1851 (new edition 1899)

Patrick Kennedy: *Legendary Fictions of the Irish Celts*, 1866

J. C. O'Hanlon ('Lageniensis'); *Irish Local Legends*, 1896, *Irish Folklore*, 1870

Gerald Griffin: *Tales of a Jury-Room*

William Larminie: *West Irish Folk Tales and Romances*, 1893

Jeremiah Curtin: *Tales of the Irish Fairies*, 1895

Joseph Jacobs: *Celtic Fairy Tales*, 1892

Edmund Leamy: *Irish Fairy Tales*, 1894

Alice Furlong: *Tales of Fairy Folks, Queens and Heroes*

T. W. Rolleston: *Myths and Legends of the Celtic Realm*, 1911

James Stephens: *Irish Fairy Tales*, 1920

Lady Gregory: *Visions and Beliefs of the West of Ireland*, 1920

W. B. Yeats: *Irish Folk Stories and Fairy Tales*, 1888

Douglas Hyde: *Beside the Fire*, 1890

Seamus MacManus: *Donegal Wonder Book*, 1926, *Donegal Fairy Stories*, 1902, *Heavy Hangs the Golden Grain*, 1951

Sinead De Valera: *Irish Fairy Tales*, 1958–60

W. G. Wood-Martin: *Traces of the Elder Faiths of Ireland*, 1902

W. Y. Evan-Wentz: *The Fairy Faith in Celtic Countries*, 1909 (Reprint 1970)

E. Andrews: *Ulster Folklore*, 1913

Dermott MacManus: *The Middle Kingdom*, 1959

Sean O'Sullivan: *Folktales of Ireland*, 1966

K. M. Briggs: *The Fairies in Tradition and Literature*, 1969

(There are also many tales in old Irish magazines such as *The Penny Journal* of the 19th century)